Dick Hardy

S0-AFN-668

FOREST RANGER, AHOY!

BY THE SAME AUTHOR

Syzygy
Mirror Image
Friends Come in Boxes
The Hero of Downways
Monitor Found in Orbit
Winter's Children
The Jaws That Bite, The Claws That Catch
Hello Summer, Goodbye
Charisma
Brontomek!
The Ultimate Jungle
Neptune's Cauldron
Cat Karina
The Celestial Steam Locomotive

FOREST RANGER, AHOY!
THE MEN—THE SHIPS—THE JOB

by

Michael Coney

Illustrated by Christine Richards

PORTHOLE PRESS LTD
SIDNEY, BRITISH COLUMBIA
1983

Published by

PORTHOLE PRESS LTD.
2082 Neptune Road,
Sidney, B.C. V8L 3X9

© Michael Coney 1983
© Christine Richards 1983 (drawings)
© John Callan 1983 (maps)

All rights reserved. No part of this publication may
be reproduced, stored in a retrieval system, or
transmitted, in any form or by any means,
electronic, mechanical, photocopying, recording or
otherwise, without the prior permission of the
Copyright owner.

Published with assistance from the
British Columbia Heritage Trust

Text typeset by The Typeworks

Printed in the United States of America

Canadian Cataloguing in Publication Data

Coney, Michael, 1932 —
   Forest ranger, ahoy!

   Includes index.

   ISBN 0–919931–00–6

1. British Columbia.   Forest Service -
History.   2. Forests and forestry - British
Columbia - History. 3. Boats and boating -
British Columbia - History.   I. Title.

SD568.B7C65   354.7110682'33   C83–091307–6

This book is dedicated to
the unsung heroes of
the British Columbia Forest Service.

Acknowledgements

While I was researching and writing FOREST RANGER, AHOY! I received the unstinting help of past and present members of the B. C. Forest Service, to whom I would like to express my gratitude:

Mike Apsey, Doug Adderley, Wilf Archer, Hugh Bancroft, Norm Beazley, Gordie Buffett, Russ Campbell, Larry Coles, Barbara Davies, Hank Doerksen, Tommy Edwards, Ray Gill, Arnold Ginnever, Bordie Grant, Mike Halleran, Ron Hawkins, Vince Hernandez, Lew King, Mike Lister, Louie Lorentsen, Wally McDonald, Don Owen, John Paynter, Jim Sweet, Frank Tannock, Howard Taylor, Ivan Teale, John Thomson, Charlie Yingling and many others.

Photographs courtesy of the Ministry of Forests with the exception of those courtesy of W. Archer (pp.171, 181); M. G. Coney (pp.85, 88, 169, 215, 217); T. T. Edwards (p.73); L. Lorentsen (p.165); J. Paynter (p.57); J. Pimlott (p.113) Provincial Archives (p111) and Riv-Tow Ltd., (p. 137)

Maps by John Callan.

Contents

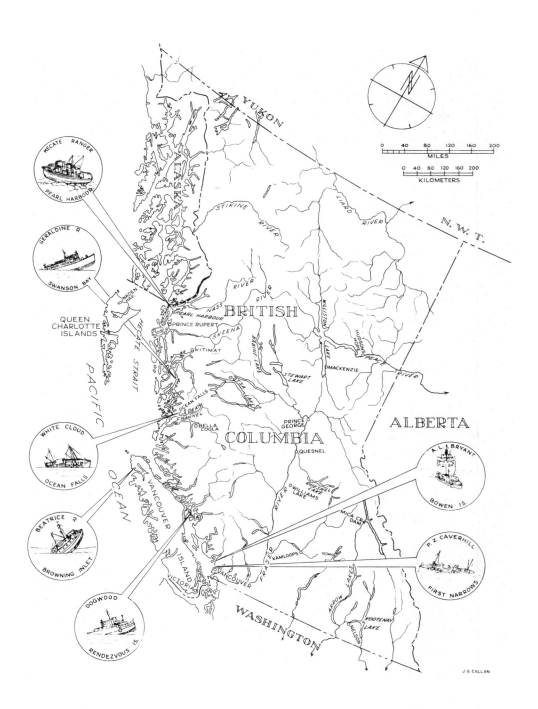

MILES
0 40 80 120 160 200

KILOMETERS
0 40 80 120 160 200

YUKON

ALASKA

N.W.T.

STIKINE RIVER

LIARD RIVER

NASS RIVER

MECATE RANGER
PEARL HARBOUR

GERALDINE R
SWANSON BAY

QUEEN
CHARLOTTE
ISLANDS

NADEN HARB.

PEARL HARBOUR
PRINCE RUPERT
SKEENA

BRITISH

KITIMAT

BABINE LAKE

STEWART LAKE

MACKENZIE

WILLISTON LAKE

HUDSONS HOPE

PEACE RIVER

HECATE STRAIT

OOSA LAKE

OCEAN FALLS
DEAN CHANNEL
BELLA COOLA

COLUMBIA

PRINCE
GEORGE

QUESNEL

ALBERTA

WHITE CLOUD
OCEAN FALLS

PACIFIC

OCEAN

VANCOUVER

QUESNEL RIVER
WILLIAMS LAKE

QUESNEL LAKE

A. L. BRYANT
BOWEN IS.

BEATRICE R
BROWNING INLET

ISLAND

VICTORIA

VANCOUVER

FRASER

KAMLOOPS

MICA CR. DAM

P. Z. CAVERHILL
FIRST NARROWS

DOGWOOD
RENDEZVOUS IS.

WASHINGTON

ARROW LAKES

NELSON

KOOTENAY LAKE

J. G. CALLAN

INTRODUCTION

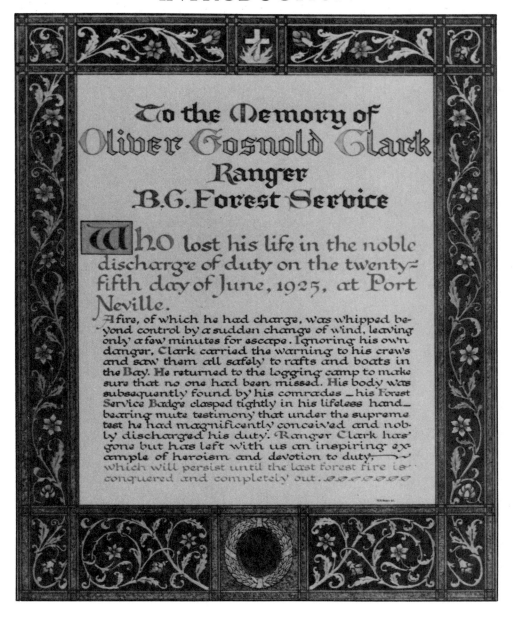

To the Memory of
Oliver Gosnold Clark
Ranger
B.C. Forest Service

Who lost his life in the noble discharge of duty on the twenty-fifth day of June, 1925, at Port Neville.

A fire, of which he had charge, was whipped beyond control by a sudden change of wind, leaving only a few minutes for escape. Ignoring his own danger, Clark carried the warning to his crews and saw them all safely to rafts and boats in the Bay. He returned to the logging camp to make sure that no one had been missed. His body was subsequently found by his comrades — his Forest Service Badge clasped tightly in his lifeless hand — bearing mute testimony that under the supreme test he had magnificently conceived and nobly discharged his duty. Ranger Clark has gone but has left with us an inspiring example of heroism and devotion to duty, which will persist until the last forest fire is conquered and completely out.

It all started one April evening in 1977, on the ferry between Kelsey Bay and Beaver Cove. As I watched the darkening islands slip by, John was describing the history of this part of the British Columbian coast, and the Forest Service boats, some long gone, which had plied these waters. He had an inexhaustible fund of anecdotes, and I remember thinking it was a pity all this history was going to waste. Somebody ought to be taking it down.

Suddenly he said:

"Over there, on that island, Oliver Clark was burned to death."

"Oliver Clark?"

"He was a Ranger back in the Twenties."

"How did he get burned?"

"A forest fire broke out near Port Neville, and it was partly fought from boats. I understand that Oliver Clark had instructed an assistant to evacuate the logging community from Port Neville because the fire was threatening to engulf it. This was apparently done. Nevertheless Oliver Clark felt obliged to go back and check things out for himself. Why he became entrapped in the fire I am not aware . . . "

Behind his careful, pedantic words there was a story. The Twenties. The primitive equipment, the rough-and-ready methods. The teamwork, the men depending on one another for their very lives. And one man alone, walking into the inferno, imbued with a sense of duty, concerned for the lives of others . . .

Now John was talking again, and he was watching me closely.

"They found the body of Oliver Clark on the beach, later. He was draped over a log, and all the clothes had been burned off him . . .

"And clasped in his hand was his Forest Service badge."

*　　*　　*　　*　　*　　*

"Yes, the part about the badge is a little excessive," John said. "But you have to understand, those were lyrical days. Men walking alone among the tall trees and the mountains. Rangers rode horses, in those days. They wrote poetry."

2   *"It was the least I could do."*

Introduction

"Poetry?" I had difficulty in visualizing today's Ranger barking orders over the radio in his four-wheel drive, then going home and penning beautiful words about trickling brooks and limpid pools.

"You've probably never heard of the 'Root and Branch', said John. "It was the original Forest Service newsletter, back in the Twenties. You should read it. It gives you an entirely different perspective. The story of Oliver Clark is in there, somewhere. I'm surprised you haven't heard of him. After all, the Americans have their Davy Crockett and General Custer. I've often thought of Oliver Clark as our own folk hero."

"I think the badge is too much."

"There was an interesting sequel. An illuminated scroll was ordered by the Premier of the day and hung in the V. C.'s gallery of the Legislative Buildings — Clark was the only non-military person so honoured. A boat was named after him. Then in the Fifties his niece came from Ontario — she'd been raised on the legend of Uncle Oliver — and she asked to see the scroll. But they couldn't find it. It had disappeared in the course of renovations. There was a tremendous hue and cry. In the end it turned up at the Forest Service Training School, and I don't know if the girl ever did get to see it. By then we'd disposed of the boat *Oliver Clark* and the new owners had renamed it. It was as if Uncle Oliver had never been. About that time we acquired a new launch, however, so I christened it the *Oliver Clark II*. It was the least I could do."

John had worked for the Forest Service since 1948, finally achieving the title of Superintendent of Marine Services. Like all good headquarters men, he spent much of his time trying to protect his authority from erosion by Regional Managers. One small responsibility he cherished was the right to bestow names upon the Forest Service boats.

"When I came on the scene they were pretty well settled with Pacific Coast trees like the Douglas Fir and the Western Hemlock, and with some of the family names of senior officials and their children. But I don't like naming boats after people. You can upset those who get left out." He chuckled. "And you can find yourself stuck with names like the *P. Z. Caverhill*, which I always thought was a trifle bizarre. So I kept to trees until I ran out of names. Then I had to resort to sub-species and even shrubs."

But he knew when to stop.

"Finally I was face to face with the probability of an M.V. *Creeping Red Whortleberry* or worse, an M. V. *Cascara*. So I began using titles like *Forest Cruiser*, *Forest Ranger* and so on. And I adopted the principle of naming only boats with inboard engines."

"So *Oliver Clark II* was your only exception?" I asked.

"It was in a good cause. There is a further exception—the boat on Quesnel Lake. It used to be the *Mountain Ash III*, but the District asked my approval to rename her the *Francis Lynn*. Lynn was a popular Ranger who had been very active in promoting awareness of safety precautions. He was building his own log house when, paradoxically enough, he was killed by a falling log. This was very sad and the District wanted to name a boat after him because he was so well thought of. I advised against it, because it would create an awkward precedent, and we didn't want to find ourselves saddled at some future date with another *P. Z. Caverhill*. But I was overridden, and they employed a professional signwriter who did a very nice job."

He displayed no rancour. It was dark now, and a single light gleamed on the distant shore, like an eternal flame to the memory of Oliver Clark. I wondered about his deed. What really happened? Would a present-day Clark have the same sense of duty? And if a present-day Clark had been killed, would he have been venerated as a hero or condemned for recklessness? Did he really have a badge in his hand, or was that written in by some reporter more in tune with the sentiments of the day than I was?

We sat down. I wondered who P. Z. Caverhill was, and what had happened to the boat named after him. And all those other people who had given their names to boats John had mentioned during our many talks: the *Beatrice R*, the *Eva R*, the *A. L. Bryant*, the *Lillian D*. Who were the people—and perhaps more interestingly, what happened to all those beautiful old boats that had served the forests in days gone by? Some of them were still working, venerable wooden hulls shouldering their way through the coastal waters even to this day; the *Oliver Clark II* was built in 1938, and still worked out of Bella Coola. Others had been sold: the glorious *Syrene*.

"How many boats does the Forest Service have, John?" I asked.

"Over three hundred, all told. That includes riverboats and small runabouts. About fifteen of them are the big coastal Ranger launches and crew boats, up to sixty-five feet long. Then there are all the Assistant Ranger launches—maybe another two dozen. Most of those are timber construction, and some of them are getting a little tired. We're coming to the end of an era, Mike."

"Someday, before it's too late, I'd like to write a book about them," I said.

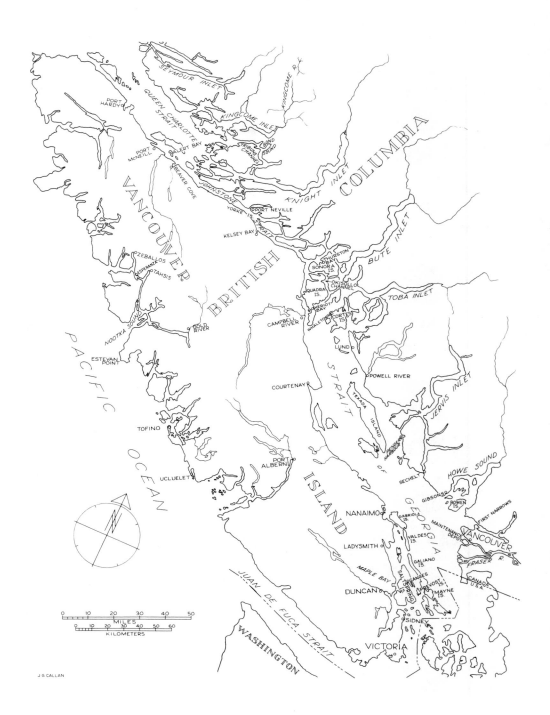

SEYMOUR INLET

PORT
HARDY

KINGCOME INLET

KINGCOME R.

QUEEN CHARLOTTE STRAIT

BRITISH
COLUMBIA

PORT
McNEILL

ALERT BAY

BEAVER COVE

BOND
SOUND

TRIBUNE
CHANNEL

KNIGHT INLET

JOHNSTONE STRAIT

YORKE IS.

PORT NEVILLE

KELSEY BAY

VANCOUVER

BUTE INLET

ZEBALLOS

ESPERANZA
TAHSIS

THURSTON
ISLAND
SONORA
IS.

OKISOLLO
CHANNEL

QUADRA
IS.

TOBA INLET

HERIOT
BAY

GOLD
RIVER

CAMPBELL
RIVER

WHALETOWN

CORTES
IS.

NOOTKA SOUND

LUND

ESTEVAN
POINT

POWELL RIVER

COURTENAY

STRAIT

TEXADA ISLAND

JERVIS INLET

PACIFIC

TOFINO

NORTHWEST
HARBOUR

OCEAN

SECHELT

HOWE SOUND

PORT
ALBERNI

GIBSONS

UCLUELET

OF

BOWEN
IS.

FIRST NARROWS

ISLAND

GEORGIA

NANAIMO

GABRIOLA
IS.

VANCOUVER

MAINTENANCE
DEPOT

LADYSMITH

VALDES
IS.

FRASER R.

GALIANO
IS.

CANADA
USA

MAPLE BAY

SALT SPRING

GANGES

PREVOST
IS.

MAYNE
IS.

DUNCAN

JUAN DE FUCA STRAIT

SIDNEY

WASHINGTON

VICTORIA

MILES
0 10 20 30 40 50

KILOMETERS
0 10 20 30 40 50 60

J.G. CALLAN

GENESIS

In the beginning there were the *Alanbee*, the *Kiora*, and the *R. J. Skinner*.

When the Forest Branch was created in 1911 these three launches were already in use. The *Alanbee* was stationed at Mayne Island and patrolled the Canada—U.S. boundary in the hope of preventing the illicit export of logs. The *Kiora* was used for inspection of applications for timber. The *R. J. Skinner* plied the coast from Vancouver north to Seymour Inlet, examining hand-loggers' licenses, dealing with trespasses, and enforcing the Timber-mark Act. North of Seymour Inlet the work was carried out by an Acting Inspector with a chartered boat.

No photographs of the *Alanbee* have come to light. The *Kiora*, however, is shown as a trim craft of around thirty-six feet with the wheelhouse well forward, a long, low coach roof and a square stern, foreshadowing in some ways the classic lines of the later Blimps.

The appearance of the *R. J. Skinner* was, in contrast, grotesque. In a photograph of the fleet at Thurston Bay she can be seen centre stage, towering menacingly over her companions like an aging prima donna. Another photograph shows her to be about fifty-five feet overall with a tall, stark wheelhouse, a long flat-topped coach roof, and a short foredeck with a human body dangling from the bow. It may be that the photograph depicts a tragic incident from the past: the recovery of a body from the deep. On the hand the body may have been alive and well, merely frozen by the camera as he struggled to jerk the anchor free from an obstruction on the sea bed. We shall never know.

The *R. J. Skinner* was built in 1909, a full year before the *Alanbee* and the *Kiora*, for the Department of Lands which at that time was responsible for timber. She was named after the Provincial Timber Inspector of the day. Under her Master, F. McKay, she was a busy ship with a fair share of problems, and McKay's biggest problem was the engine.

"It was built by a man named Cowie when he was experimenting with gasoline engines," runs one unhappy letter. "The Captain feels she may break down sometime when he cannot save her from being wrecked, as she has broken down on a number of occasions and was saved by using the dinghy." In 1912 a new Union 35 h.p. engine was installed, and she proceeded about

"The appearance of the R. J. Skinner *was ... grotesque."*

her duties with a new confidence—although not always as reliably as some people would have liked.

"WHERE IS SHE?" ran a plaintive telegram from a Ranger stranded at Heriot Bay on September 14, 1914. "NEED CLOTHES AND MONEY." We hope that the first thing McKay did, on picking up the naked and shivering Ranger, was to lead him below, wrap him in a blanket and give him a shot of rum.

In fact he may have been out of luck with the blanket. "Please supply blankets," wrote Ranger Penny on winter patrol with the *Embree* in the Charlottes in 1920, but Mr. E. C. Manning, District Forester, concerned with setting a precedent, replied that it was not his policy to provide bedding on the boats.

They were bleak and lonely patrols in those days, cruising the northern coasts under the shadow of the tall trees, but they passed without notable incident until July 4, 1921, when the *Skinner* was on the ways at Vancouver Shipyards having her fuel tanks replaced. One of the new tanks proved to have a leak, and a shipyard worker took an acetylene torch to it. In the resultant explosion two men were injured, the cabin roof was split open and all the windows were blown out. When the workers crept back to the smoking carcass, they found extensive dry rot behind the cracked panels and blistered paint. The yard, profiting from disaster, was authorized to replace the decay-

9

ing timbers and, a few weeks later, the marine surveyor was moved to certify her as being "IN A STAUNCH AND SEAWORTHY CONDITION."

His optimism was ill-founded, and in October 1922 SEVERE HULL ROT AND HOGGING was diagnosed in an inspector's report. By now she no longer enjoyed the status of having a captain, and Engineer Caddell was in charge with a single crew member known cryptically as "the cook". She was patched up and sent back on duty.

On January 16, 1923 she rammed the launch *Daphrona* near Gibsons, while the cook was at the wheel. Within a month she was in trouble again, having collided with the tug *Canadian*. Once again, the accident report revealed that the cook was steering. Mr. Manning, in a letter to Mr. P. Z. Caverhill, the Chief Forester, metaphorically threw up his hands in despair.

"It is practically impossible," he wrote, "to secure a cook who is a competent navigator."

By 1924 the *Skinner* was being used at the northern end of Vancouver Island, cruising timber sales, "and after June 15 1924 we do not particularly require this boat," wrote the Ranger callously. In October of that year the *R. J. Skinner* was sold to Mr. Oscar Ozana, a handlogger from Vancouver who made the only offer for her: $1500. He renamed her the *Annie Sophia* and she faded quietly from the scene.

* * * * * *

The three coast launches were not enough to handle the growing volume of work, so an order for reinforcements was placed with the Hinton Electric Company of Victoria in 1912. This called for two fifty-four foot and four thirty-six foot boats to the design of the naval architect E. B. Schock. "The type of construction was plain and solid and the total price of the six boats was $28,636," states a later report.

Meanwhile the original three boats were augmented by a succession of rented craft. The *Eleanor Mac* was one, and another was the *Export Patrol*. This latter twenty-seven foot launch was at first chartered from its owner, one Captain Kidd, who stayed with his boat and assumed the title of Export Patrol Officer. In 1918 the Forest Branch bought the boat outright, and Mr. G. Wallace took the title.

Shortly afterwards, a Branch official inspected the vessel and commented on her poor condition—and, indeed, extended his remarks to cover G. Wallace as well.

"The Eva R *was a long-lived boat."*

"Mr. Wallace seems to be rather in the dark as to his real duties other than examining booms passing. Also he was rather nervous at having to run an engine which he had had handed over to him with very few instructions. Of course, his nerves, I imagine, are not all they should be after shell shock, but I think he will gain confidence. I also imagine that the remarks of some of the inhabitants do not tend to make him any more confident." Clearly there is a sad story behind those words and the *Export Patrol*, crumbling with dry rot, was sold out of service in 1920.

Other boats were borrowed; the *Faloma* was one such. The Forest Branch used her by courtesy of her true owners, the Fisheries Department. She had a chequered career and although stated to be 'comfortable' and 'larger than the *Skinner*', she was only capable of a dawdling five m.p.h. Moreover, she became notorious for heavy repair bills. In 1916 Fisheries made a gift of her to Forests, but her days were already numbered. Foreshadowing the present practice of willing one's body to medical research, the Forest Branch gave the worn-out *Faloma* to the Provincial Board of Health in 1917.

By 1913 the Hinton Electric Company had delivered four of the six boats ordered: two of fifty-four foot and two of thirty-six foot, the latter being the *Eva R* and the *Geraldine R*. In the following year the other two thirty-six footers were delivered: the *Beatrice R* and the *Eunice B*. All four were pretty little ships, double-ended, long coach roofs echoing the contour of the deck line, with a fairly low forward wheelhouse and a short foredeck. They were similar to the earlier *Kiora*, although with a more pronounced sheer.

Like the *Beatrice R*, the *Eva R* was a long-lived boat. She spent her life working in and around Thurston Bay and other stations of the southern coast until her final sale in 1949. She had a fine seaworthy hull but, in her later years, a nasty little quirk. Louie Lorentsen, retired Ranger, told me about it.

"My Assistant Ranger brought the *Eva R* from Vancouver to Cracroft when I took over Chatham Channel station. I was waiting for him at the dock. Well, he came in fine, but the clutch stuck in forward when he tried to throw her into reverse. He came sailing under the wharf and folded the davits right over. He jumped off, and the *Eva R* came crunching to a halt somewhere under there."

This was a frequent problem. The clutch would jam, and it could not be freed in a hurry. Shortly after this opening foray the *Eva R* had the temerity to ram the fleet's flagship—the dowager *Syrene* under the command of her re-doubtable skipper, Art Bouch.

"We had an Assistant Ranger called Mark," said Louie's wife Bunny. "He used to operate her, and he never turned a hair when these things happened." The *Eva R* would come gliding swiftly towards the dock, the clutch would jam, and she would sail rapidly by while people hurled ropes to and fro in the manner of cowhands trying to lasso a runaway steer.

"Mark took it all in his stride," said Bunny. "One time we got a stern line on her but it was too late, and Mark just stood on deck with his hands on his hips, watching her run onto the rocks. Then he stepped ashore."

"She was a jittery boat, too," added Louie. "The shaft was misaligned. I complained about that boat a lot. Finally, just before she went in for overhaul, I loosened the bolts that held the bearings and jimmied the shaft even further out of alignment. I figured that way they'd have to fix her."

He sighed. "But they still said there was nothing wrong with her."

The sticking clutch was a family trait. Mike Lister operated the *Beatrice R* towards the end of her Forest Service days at Sechelt. "She was very low in the stern and the slop would come right over it. But her worst problem was the clutch. If you ran for anything approaching an hour the plates would stick and stall the engine—at that time a Gardner diesel. I recall Vince Hernandez getting rather upset once, and writing to Bob Swan about it. He wanted a start button in the wheelhouse, so he could get the engine going again in a panic situation. Bob Swan wrote back, saying that he couldn't have his button be-cause the operator had to go into the engineroom anyway, to use the decom-pression levers before he started up—besides which, diesels don't stall." He

The fleet at Thurston Bay in the Twenties

laughed. "We'd never used any decompression levers. We didn't know what they looked like."

John Paynter threw some light on this. "Bob Swan liked to make people go to the engineroom because it meant they'd notice if there was water in there. If they could start the boat from the wheelhouse, they might not go into the engine room for weeks on end, and the boat could be sinking under them."

* * * * * *

1917 found the *Geraldine R* at Thurston Bay, being refitted. Up to that point she had been stationed in Vancouver but now, gleaming with new paint, she headed into the stormy northern waters for a spell of duty at Prince Rupert with Ranger Williams. Her engineer was one Campbell, a good Scots name which the reader will do well to remember. After performing adequately she was transferred to Swanson Bay in 1921, and her troubles began. On October 5th of that year it was discovered that she had suffered severe and inexplicable damage to her rudder and propeller. Everybody pointed at everybody else. Manning, the District Forester of the day, reported:

"I can find nothing definite, and presume the matter must be dropped. Engineer Campbell might know something about it, but since we let him out for drunkenness, his knowledge goes with him."

On November 21st. of that same year the engine water jacket froze and burst, causing considerable damage, and also causing the finger to be pointed at her new operators, Ranger Henning and Engineer Scott. However, during the course of a complete rebuilding at Thurston Bay in 1922, all her water passages were found to be scaled up and it was felt that Engineer Scott could well have been deceived by this factor, when he thought he'd drained her. The accusations were withdrawn.

Back at Swanson Bay, however, in the hands of a new crew—Ranger Gritten and Engineer Allen—the *Geraldine R* met her doom.

＊　＊　＊　＊　＊　＊

On December 19th., 1923, Ranger Gritten received instructions to have emergency local repairs made to his troublesome charge. The Swanson Bay marine shop could not spare the men, so on the following morning the *Geraldine R* limped off in the direction of Butedale, where Gritten hoped facilities would be available.

Six miles north of Swanson Bay the *Geraldine R* stopped in the water, rolling with the swell.

The engine was silent. Hearing a shout from Engineer Allen, Gritten left the wheel and went into the engine room.

"There's water in the gas," Allen told him. He was draining the feed tank, from time to time tasting the liquid as it flowed into the bilge. More than a gallon of water had been drained off before a small proportion of gas became noticeable. Allen then drained the watery mixture into a can until he judged the gas to be pure. He threw the contents of the can over the side.

Leaving Allen swabbing the floor, Gritten returned to the wheel. After a few coughs the engine fired up, and the *Geraldine R* resumed her voyage.

Ten minutes later Gritten heard another shout.

"The engine's on fire!"

Grabbing the Pyrene on his way through the cabin, Gritten arrived in the engineroom to find Allen already pumping the other extinguisher at a fire which had a good hold around the engine and seemed to be spreading under the floor. In less than a minute dense fumes forced the men from the cabin. As

"All four were pretty little ships."

they retreated, the engine room and cabin exploded into a roaring inferno. They fought the fire from the deck, while the flames raced towards the main fuel tank.

The men lowered the dinghy, barely having time to snatch the compass and binoculars from the wheelhouse before that, too, became engulfed in flames. Then they rowed to a safe distance and watched. By this time the *Geraldine R* was near the middle of Graham Reach, about half a mile offshore. The tide was setting away from the beach at Indian River, nearly a mile away. An up-channel breeze was freshening. It was clearly impossible to tow the *Geraldine R* ashore with the dinghy.

The two men rowed disconsolately to a nearby mining camp, returning to the smoking wreck later in the camp launch. By this time the *Geraldine R* had burned to the waterline, with the bow and stern framework still smouldering. The blackened engine could be seen squatting among the skeletal remains.

Then, as the camp launch closed in, the *Geraldine R* sank.

*   *   *   *   *   *

An engine backfire had touched off the blaze. There was no doubt that the engine of the *Geraldine R* was more than due for an overhaul. However, the practice of draining water off the gas tanks into the bilge—a common but unauthorized procedure in those days—was primarily the cause.

In mitigation Ranger Gritten pointed out that another launch was lost by fire on the same day, "and the complete destruction of the launch was even quicker than in my case. Also another launch owned by a local logger was burned about a week ago. This was also a total loss."

But the logic of his plea escaped the Chief Forester, and Ranger Gritten was severely censured. Engineer Allen quit.

THE ILL-FATED SHIP

By the end of World War I the Forest Branch had developed a fair-sized fleet to handle the various jobs up and down the coast. Logging was on the upsurge and new Ranger Stations were being opened to handle the resulting administration work. New boats were bought or built to cope with the growing transportation needs of the Branch.

The *R. J. Skinner*, the *Alanbee* and the *Kiora* were still going strong, albeit a little long in the tooth. The *Faloma* had gone, but the Hinton Electric boats were in service and had been augmented by four smaller boats, the *Gwen*, *Hermes*, *Georgia*, and *Jean L.*

In 1918 the *Embree* arrived, thirty-one feet five inches at the waterline, with a beam of ten feet three inches and a draft of four feet four inches. Bought from George Wray in Jervis Inlet, she had been built in New Brunswick in 1909. She had a 16 h.p. Union engine, a neat but low wheelhouse with a short foredeck and a long cabin, the roof of which rose towards the stern and gave her a wedge-shaped appearance.

She was reputed to be a fine sea-boat—and she needed to be, since she was to operate in the Charlottes. She was rebuilt shortly after purchase with a higher coach roof; a 24 h.p. Eastern Standard engine was installed centrally and the galley moved further forward, immediately behind the engine. With this new configuration she was not dissimilar in appearance to the Hinton Electric sisters, except for her large rectangular windows.

The Ill-Fated Ship

Ranger Penny was a resourceful man. His temerity in asking for blankets has already been mentioned, and on an earlier occasion he had asked for a lighting system. Then in August of 1920 he got caught in a bad south-easter and was forced to beach the *Embree*, in the process losing a borrowed rowboat. Capitalizing on this incident he ordered a new ignition system. He furnished Headquarters with a list of electrical requirements, and wrote: "This combination of dry cells and magneto does not produce an efficient spark, result is lack of speed and the uncertainty of never knowing if you will reach your destination."

He had underestimated Headquarters, who wrote back: "It is noted that the list of equipment needed for your *ignition system* is practically identical with what was asked for in your request of December 9th., 1919 for a *lighting system*."

But *Embree* was due for a complete refit. The lighting system was installed in the course of this, in 1922. She spent her remaining years in northern waters with some incident, grounding herself in September of 1926 on a falling tide and subsequently being swamped. In the same year she broke down at the mouth of the Skeena and drifted for several hours before taking a tow. Finally taken to Thurston Bay for overhaul in 1930 she was found to be not worth repairing and was sold to Mr. R. Miller of Hemming Bay for $650.

Four further coastal launches are briefly referred to in the skimpy records of the day; all were in service around 1921. The *Idonno* was based at Whaletown in the care of Ranger Fred O'Grady. The *Elmera* was first mentioned in the Annual Return of 1924 and for much of her time she worked out of Lund. Photographs show her to be a stylish double-ender of around thirty-seven feet. The *Western Hemlock* was bought immediately after World War I and fades from the picture around 1925. She was about thirty feet long with an aft wheelhouse and a flush deck. She can be seen at the dockside in photographs of Thurston Bay and it is known that she was re-engined there in 1922. Details of her operational life are shrouded in mystery, however, as are details of the *Walrondo II*, another thirty-footer of that era.

*　*　*　*　*　*

You have heard about the four Hinton Electric sisters: the *Eva R*, the *Geraldine R*, the *Beatrice R* and the *Eunice B*. You have also heard that two larger boats were ordered from the same company. These were delivered in

"In 1918 the Embree *arrived."*

1913 and given the names *Euclataw* and *Leila R*. Each had a tall, boxy wheel-house and a flush, raised deck aft of this with a long row of portholes and a rounded stern. In later days they sported funnels behind the wheelhouse, giving them the appearance of scaled-down ocean liners.

The *Euclataw* spent most of her life at Ocean Falls and waters north; a report from R. C. St. Clair in 1922 describes her as 'palatial' after a rebuild at Thurston Bay in 1921. Rumours of her tendency to crash-dive in heavy seas were strengthened by a report in the Forest Service Newsletter of March 25th., 1940:

> "The launch *Euclataw*, under the command of 'Rear-Admiral' James Blake, was brought down from Ocean Falls to Vancouver for overhaul. Reports indicate that this famous conveyor of Forest Service officials has become slightly stuck-up as a result of a face-lifting job; at any rate, they claim she will keep her nose above water now. When you see Jim Blake ask him what he did with his meals while crossing Queen Charlotte Sound."

Tommy Edwards, one-time Superintendent of the Forest Service Mainte-nance Depot, told me, "Jim Blake was a man you couldn't scare. Coming across Queen Charlotte Sound in that old *Euclataw* he hit a sea that broke over him so hard that it drove the wheelhouse back on the hull, so you could fit a pack of cigarettes between the front of the wheelhouse and the deck!"

The *Euclataw* disappeared from the scene in the Forties, sold as a towboat after a long and successful career.

Her sister, the *Leila R*, was a different character.

The Ill-Fated Ship

Her story opens soon after delivery in 1913, when she is sitting at Thurston Bay under the command of Captain Eden, awaiting engine parts and a cook before she sets off on a month's cruise of the Campbell River area. "COOK SERIOUSLY ILL NOT FIT FOR TRIP" ran the telegram Eden sent to Headquarters.

In due course both engine parts and replacement cook were received. After completion of the Campbell River cruise, the *Leila R* headed for Prince Rupert, which was to be her home base. Captain Eden departed, after leaving his mark. "The launch was left in a very filthy condition by Captain Eden," complained Mr. H. S. Irwin, the District Forester. He was, however, mollified by the fact that in rough weather in the Sound the boat 'behaved splendidly.' The following year the same District Forester reported to the Chief Forester on *Leila R*'s performance to date. "The launch is very seaworthy but not comfortable to live on. The deck isn't tight . . . Blankets get damp and uncomfortable. Oil heaters smoke too much and make the air unbreathable . . . "

The seeds of discontent were sown.

Now under Captain Archie with a crew of cook and deck hand, the *Leila R* frequently undertook the stormy voyage to the Queen Charlottes. The inclement weather did not suit her and a history of cracked cylinders began to build up. On August 14th., 1918 she suffered her first serious accident, striking a rock at Skidegate Channel, badly damaging the propeller and shaft, and splitting the keel. She was repaired and put back into service, but an ominous note was struck by a letter from Prince Rupert to the Chief Forester which cast serious doubts on the boat's future.

"If the proposition is to sell the *Leila R*, certainly we shall take the chance of running through the summer without a spare propeller . . . "

In January 1921, the *Leila R* disappeared. With storms lashing the Hecate Strait she was reported overdue in Prince Rupert on a voyage from the Charlottes. Chilling rumours circulated around the town, and whispers reached the ear of the Chief Forester. The days went by and as the storms abated the search parties set off. They found no sign of the ship. The Prince Rupert office reported that the *Leila R* had been lost at sea with all hands.

Then, on January 21st., 1921, the Chief Forester received a telegram.

"REFERENCE REPORTED LOSS LEILA R MURDER AT MORESBY ISLAND PROVINCIAL POLICE REQUESTED USE OUR BOAT LAY SHELTER BANKS ISLAND OVER WEEK UNABLE TO CROSS HECATE STRAITS BAD WEATHER . . . "

"The Elmera *was a stylish double-ender."*

Behind these words lay a story which was seized upon by the *Vancouver Sun:*

"A record of adventure at sea which would rival thrilling seafaring tales of fiction is told by Captain Batt of the *Leila R* while bound for Cumshewa Inlet, Queen Charlotte Islands.

"The *Leila R* left Prince Rupert bound for the Islands on January 6th. On board was Constable Ackroyd of the Provincial police force whose mission was to take to Prince Rupert an alleged murderer, Holmes by name, who is said to have killed a settler by the name of Booth in a quarrel over a woman, and who was held at Queen Charlotte City. The crew of the gas boat consisted of Pilot Leighton and Engineer Doreen. In Hecate Straits the little boat ran into dirty weather and when half way across to Queen Charlotte Islands lost her way and, according to the story told, drifted for hours in a big sea in utter darkness.

"When the boat had been twenty-four hours adrift all hands were said to have abandoned hope of ever reaching land. The blow developed into the worst storm that ever swept the Straits. With a fast-ebbing supply of food, prospects were none too pleasant. Only through the heroic efforts of all hands was the tiny craft kept afloat until finally she ran aground on what turned out to be Banks Island, Latitude 53 degrees, 20 minutes N., longitude 130 degrees West.

"Failure of the *Leila R* to report caused considerable excitement at Prince Rupert and a rescuing party was sent out on the *Narbethong* including a number of Provincial policemen. No trace of the *Leila R* was to be found and she was for a time given up for lost.

"Today Provincial police headquarters learned that the *Leila R* had gone aground on Banks Island and the captain and his men were able to land. For six days they were marooned on the island, suffering severe hardships.

"The *Narbethong* reached Cumshewa Inlet and the constable took the prisoner aboard and he is now at Prince Rupert jail."

*　　*　　*　　*　　*　　*

A stirring yarn indeed, although one wonders at the astringent properties of the Hecate Straits which shrank the fifty-four foot *Leila R* to a little boat, and ultimately to a tiny craft.

The *Leila R* was salvaged and examined. The Inspector's report boded ill. "Hull: leaky, worm-eaten around waterline, some dry rot where cabin joins deck, bilge up to floor every 24 hours . . . ." These defects became inconsequential, however, as *Leila's* next exploit was reported by telegram from Prince Rupert to the Chief Forester on May 31st., 1921:

> "THIS MORNING REAR GASOLINE TANKS LEILA R EX-
> PLODED FIRE GUTTED AT LEAST REAR OF VESSEL AND
> CABIN BOAT WAS SCUTTLED AND SANK BETWEEN FIFTEEN
> AND TWENTY FEET LOW TIDE IMPOSSIBLE TO SAY EX-
> TENT DAMAGE AM ENDEAVOURING TO SECURE BIDS FOR
> RAISING HER ONLY ONE SO FAR RECEIVED FOR
> UNREASONABLE PRICE FIVE HUNDRED DOLLARS WILL
> WIRE YOU TOMORROW BEST OFFER IF DESIRABLE INSPEC-
> TOR BLAKE SEE BOAT BEFORE DECIDING REPAIR HER
> PLEASE COME AT ONCE AS FIELD WORK PILING UP AND
> QUICK DECISION NECESSARY SENDING FULL WRITTEN
> REPORT CREW SAFE."

Correspondence flitted to and fro, and the facts of the accident became known. It seemed that Engineer Campbell, later of the *Geraldine R* and 'let out for drunkenness,' had been burning paint from the *Leila's* woodwork. In his alcoholic enthusiasm it seemed possible — although it was never proved — that he had applied his blow-torch to the gasoline tank vent pipe. The District Forester sprang to his defence.

"He is an old employee of the Branch, and barring a certain tendency to drink to excess on occasion, which has not yet seriously interfered with his work, I consider him a good employee. I do not feel justified in parting with the services of a man who I value rather highly, and who has during the past three weeks done the job of painting and varnishing on the *Leila* which would do credit to anyone."

A pity indeed that the *Leila* was twenty feet below the waves, so Campbell's workmanship was not available for inspection. After she was raised, Jim Blake gave his verdict, which was transmitted to the Chief:

"CONSIDERING BOAT AGE BELIEVE ABOUT EIGHT YEARS THINK MONEY PROBABLY BETTER SPENT BUILDING NEW BOAT."

The Chief Forester had other ideas:

"...BOAT ONLY EIGHT YEARS OLD AND WITH COMPLETE OVERHAUL PLANKING AND REMOVING ANY DRY ROT HULL SHOULD BE AS GOOD AS NEW BLAKE ONLY EXPERT ON ENGINES NOT HULL..."

The example of the sister-ship *Euclataw*, quietly going about her duties at Ocean Falls, probably influenced the Chief Forester.

The accident report made exciting reading. Said Thomas Roberts: "I heard an explosion which backed me up against the wall and on looking aft I saw flames and started for one of the fire extinguishers. Seeing a burst of flame through the steps behind which were situated the gasoline tanks I turned around and rushed out on deck...I saw Mr. Campbell was safe and looked for Temple, then jumped overboard."

Herbert Temple knew even less. "While I was painting, the first thing I felt was a blow on the side of my head and then I found myself in the water having been blown from the deck, then I swam ashore to the rocks and was picked up by a boat."

J. B. McKay testified, "The first I heard was an explosion in the rear part of the boat, the next thing the cook was blown up against me...I saw Mr. Campbell running across the scow and jumping into the water, his back was on fire...The marine men scuttled the *Leila*."

And Campbell himself: "The gasoline tanks below the rear deck on which I was standing suddenly exploded and I was blown off onto an adjoining scow."

The *Leila R* was returned to service by the end of the year, but at high cost, and Captain Archie resumed command. In her final years she was visited by George P. Melrose, later to become Deputy Minister of Lands, who wrote:

"I transferred to the *Leila R* — Prince Rupert's H. Q. launch — and spent a couple of days visiting numerous camps on the Island, finishing up at Port Clements. Here is a town of old abandoned sawmills and houses that, in War days, was a bustling place of large population. Now Ranger Scott occupies the hotel and he has a choice of about fifteen beds in which to sleep...

The Euclataw *and* Leila R *at Shoal in* 1914

"After two days around Cumshewa, the storm-bound *Leila R* turned up and we went on to Thurston Harbour. On the way a shore trip was taken to cruise a timber sale. Half-way though the wind came up, and on account of the exposed nature of the anchorage we had to cut and run, leaving a stand of some mighty fine spruce that was a pleasure to cruise. Illustrating what Penny and a few more Rangers are up against, we weren't half-way to Thurston Harbour, until the boat was taking them blue over the pilot house! Even the large H. Q. launch got a good shaking up—what Penny would have received in his little *Embree* can be imagined! I believe such sudden storms are all too frequent and have heard several tales of Penny's narrow escapes. Apparently good seamanship alone got him by. He travels alone, at that."

But the *Leila R* was reaching the end of her career. On December 18th., 1923, Mr. E. C. Manning at Prince Rupert wrote, "The *Leila R* has been in service now for ten years and serious consideration must be given to replacing her with a new boat similar to the new *B. C. Forester* which is being built at Thurston Bay . . . Her decks around the pilot house have been seriously affected by dry rot and it is very probable that in another year she may require extensive reconstruction."

25

She had one last flirt with disaster. On January 5th., 1924, a south-easter sprang up and *Leila R* ran for shelter in Jap Inlet. Captain Archie moored to a dolphin but his position was exposed, the wind freshened and in the early evening the dolphin carried away. The *Leila R* got underway and, making for the head of the inlet where Captain Archie knew of a sheltered spot, struck a rock on the falling tide. As the ship began to list, the crew closed all ports and went ashore. The wind strengthened further. Alarmed, Captain Archie fought his way back to the *Leila* and, in his own words, "found water pouring in at every crack." Bailing began. Later, as the tide rose, they got her upright. Engineer Cook worked on the flooded engine for several hours before finally getting it going and, leaking like a sieve, the *Leila R* headed home.

There was a note of resignation in Mr. Manning's letter to Mr. Caverhill: "It will be noted that the *Leila* has again been on the rocks . . . "

She lasted the year through, then early in 1925 was offered up for sale. At first there were no takers. Probably her reputation as an unlucky ship was too widespread. Then in September 1925, Mr. Alfred Swanson of Prince Rupert plucked up the courage to offer $1350 for her.

Her days of service over, she went into an early retirement.

THE HERO

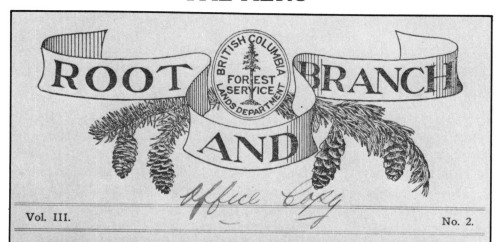

ROOT AND BRANCH

BRITISH COLUMBIA FOREST SERVICE LANDS DEPARTMENT

Office Copy

Vol. III.   No. 2.

Oliver G. Clark.

Choked and burnt in the fiery hell,
He rushed to the water's edge, and fell.
And in his hand, so tightly clasped,
We found his Badge of Service grasped
His Forest Badge as if to say,
"I've done my duty"....

                        Far away
The night winds whisper over the tide,
"He did his duty—and he died."
No nobler tribute could we give:
HE DIED THAT OTHER MEN
    MIGHT LIVE.

"How's the boat history coming along?" John Paynter asked me one day.

"Not too badly—except that whenever I seem to be hitting my stride, I have to break off and head for the Provincial Archives to look something up. It's different from writing fiction. Then it's just me and the typewriter—a straight one-on-one situation. When my knowledge isn't up to scratch, I can invent. But a history book . . . I'm surrounded by files and magazines and card-index systems and taped interviews. There's hardly room for the typewriter, and no room for me at all. I'm sitting on a stack of old photograph albums."

"But you must be finding some interesting stuff."

"Yes, but I'm not sure how to use it. A lot of interesting stuff is exciting, and anything exciting might be construed as reflecting adversely on the efficiency of the Forest Service. Exciting things should *never* happen on a boat. The last thing I want is to make the Rangers look like a bunch of jackasses."

"Slip in bits about what a grand job they're doing."

"I'll do that."

"And there are a number of stories around which reflect very much to the credit of the men. Like the time on Lake Williston, when we dropped a D9 Cat off the transporter barge into thirty feet of water."

"Sounds very commendable."

"No, it was no fault of the people involved. The bank of the lake was unstable as a result of recent inundation by the rising waters of the reservoir. The technique was to push the transporter barge into the bank and keep the engines running full ahead, then lower the ramp onto the bank and drive the equipment off. They'd done it often. But this time the bank collapsed just as they got the D9 onto the ramp. So the ramp was unsupported, and the sudden weight of the Cat uprooted the towers which raise and lower the ramp from the deck. The whole lot went over the bow. The Cat went down into thirty feet of water and began to silt over."

"Discouraging."

"So they got a crane onto the barge and a diver hooked it onto the winch of the Cat. Those Cats weigh about fifty tons, and with the silting there would be a suction factor to contend with. They started winding up on the crane until it came to a grunting stop. Then, knowing that it was just a matter of waiting for the suction to break, they sat down to eat their lunch. While they were eating, the suction released, but the boom of the crane collapsed with the shock of the recoil. It crashed to the deck in a crumpled heap. Nothing daunted—"

"I'd have been daunted," I admitted. "Irreversibly."

"They're a very resourceful, unfazeable type of man. They picked up two more D9 Cats which they placed at opposite ends of the barge, chained together. They lowered the winch wire from one Cat over the stern of the barge, hooked it to the winch of the submerged Cat and pulled it up. Just like that. Three days later the Cat was back in operation.

"This," he concluded, "is a tribute to their rough-hewn resourcefulness in what to a city person would be hopeless circumstances."

"I'll use that story," I told him gratefully.

"Now here is the real point of your book, Mike," he said seriously. "Of course we've had our accidents. But in view of our inhospitable coastline, the sudden storms, the isolated conditions, the minimal amount of training which we are able to give our men—the fact that most of them aren't boat-minded at all, but simply men of the trees forced to use boats for transport—in view of all this, they've done bloody well and we've had far fewer accidents than we have a right to expect."

"Some of our boats have qualified Masters," I said.

"Half a dozen, maybe. I'll never forget one time I went out with a Ranger in one of the smaller boats. I was just standing there in the pilot house, appreciating the romance of it all—the swish of the ocean past the hull, the cry of the gulls, the smell of salt—when this Ranger said to me, 'Would you like to take the wheel?' Well, I hesitated, Mike. I didn't want to spoil his fun. I said, 'Do you mind?' And he said, 'I'd rather you did. To me, boats are just a necessity.'"

"Maybe the title of the book should be 'The Reluctant Mariners.'"

"It sounds too negative. To the Rangers, boats are all part of the job and they take them in their stride. Next year they may be working out of some Ranger station in the dry interior, miles from the coast, miles from any kind of lake, even. They're adaptable men. There's still a touch of the romantic about them, even though they'd never admit it. By the way—talking of the old days—did you ever get to see the 'Root and Branch?'"

I told him I hadn't got around to it yet.

"It's worth your time, Mike. Talk to Susan Barker at the Ministry Library. They're sure to have copies there."

*   *   *   *   *   *

Susan showed me a short row of bound volumes and asked me in passing if I knew the old Forest Branch once had a boat called the *R. J. Skinner*. She smiled faintly as she spoke, as though the name was somehow peculiar, like the *P. Z. Caverhill*.

I sat down and began to read.

The 'Root and Branch' had been typed and run off on a duplicator with occasional simple artwork rather like a science fiction fan magazine, bound together about two dozen pages to an issue, published at irregular intervals between 1922 and 1925.

I could have read for hours.

In just three years the essence of the old Forest Branch had been captured, encapsulated. Yes, they were lyrical days and yes, Rangers wrote poetry:

"See yonder peak so grim and proud,
So silent and so lone;
Draped superb in wintry shroud,
Towering 'midst the fleecy cloud,
Tis the eagle's stately throne..."

There was much more. My own favourite depicted three weary workers with thick necks and determined jawlines surveying a landscape from which every tree had been removed, leaving but a few spindly snags. The poem's title was 'Co-operation' and its final verse read:

"So help us guard the Forest; help us keep the West
The happy home of thousands! Let each man do his best
To use the gifts of Nature on a well-ordered plan
And make, and keep our Province a Paradise for Man."

One man's hand rests on another's shoulder in a gesture of comradeship, while a third holds an axe.

As John had promised, I found plenty about the boats. The general tenor of 'Root and Branch''s contributors was affection and pride — although accidents were relentlessly reported:

"Ranger Gritten, while proceeding to a fire at Pender Harbour, ran the launch *Cherry* aground on a rock," ran an item in August 1922. Remember Ranger Gritten, who in the following year was to sink the *Geraldine R*? "Gritten is to be censured in that he was running the boat at full speed in what he knew to be dangerous waters... It took Ranger Gritten from 10 a. m. to 8

p. m. to get the *Cherry* off and beached, with detrimental results to his salary cheque."

Pride showed itself unmistakably in the attitude towards new acquisitions which displayed the Branch in a modern light. In October 1922:

"The latest addition to our fleet is named the *Cottonwood*. She is a handy little craft of 38 feet overall and 9'6" beam, with a two-cylinder 4-cycle Vivian engine which drives her at a speed of from 8-9 m. p. h. An important part of her equipment is the radio-telephone which in her case has a radius of from 40-60 miles. Her two masts (made necessary by the 'wireless' installation) and her dinghy slung inboard on davits, give her a very distinctive appearance. Douglas Fir has been used extensively in her construction. The workmanship throughout is excellent, and altogether she reflects great credit on her designer, Mr. E. B. Schock, Naval Architect of Vancouver, and her builders, Messrs. Erickson and Ball."

And she's on the cover of the next issue; a nice pen-and-ink sketch and the poem: 'The Lone Patrol.'

"Plugging along the Lone Patrol,
Now up, now down, we toss, we roll,
For the wind is blowing hard.
We hear the breakers pound and roar
Along the desolate timbered shore,
Which we are sent to guard.

We're all alone on a sullen sea
With the screaming sea-birds flying free
Beneath the leaden dome.
No human power can reach us, save
The ghostly voice on the wireless wave
That links us to our home."

Interesting items appear, bits of history slot into place, and the Chief Forester, P. Z. Caverhill contributes a chatty article entitled 'Ship-shape.' And from J. H. Blake—who, you will remember, was not an expert on hulls—these words:

"Our little fleet, almost unknown to the general public, is quietly but

"The latest additon to our fleet is named the Cottonwood.*"*

surely making its mark. What would the Forest Branch do without its gas-boats, especially on the coast? Carrying the Supervisor, Ranger or other field officer on his daily round, for scaling, cruising, forest protection and many other phases which go to make up the day's work...

"... the launches are in very much better state than at this time last year... however... two of the launches are badly marked up from caulked boots, and some are not so clean as they might be, or have been allowed to rub up against floats and booms without fenders."

J. H. Blake's rapidly-deteriorating tone now became positively menacing. "I'm going to utter a word of warning here. It has been my experience that most men are willing to be reasonable, but unhappily we still have one or two who are not, and it is to those men that this warning is directed..."

Strong words from a man proud of his fleet. One wonders what his

"Our little fleet is quietly but surely making its mark."

comments were in November 1922, when the *Alanbee* ran onto a rock off Dent Island in broad daylight. As the news item says, "The rock on which the *Alanbee* struck lies only about 160 feet off shore, and to hoist herself clear up onto it she must have been hitting a pretty fair gait . . . The officer has been suspended, pending the decision of the Court of Enquiry."

Immediately below this item is an appropriate joke. Most of the jokes in 'Root and Branch,' and there are many, tend to be unfortunate by present-day standards; usually through a lack of subtlety and almost total dependence on racial overtones. Still, lyrical days must also be simple days; "'. . . I know every shoal north of Vancouver except one,' assured Murphy. Just then the craft hit a rocky bottom and sheered sharply to the left. 'That's it now,' he said, never slackening speed a particle."

Hints on seamanship are in the 'Root and Branch,' too:

"The practice of towing dinghies in heavy weather has cost us two boats. One of them was lost last July from the *Balsam*, the other a week or two ago from the *Embree*."
There followed instructions on how not to lose the dinghy.

And social events:

"One of the attractions at the annual regatta of the Cowichan Yacht Club, held at Cowichan Bay, Friday, was the motorboat *Balsam*, Mr. Warburton, Forest Ranger of the Provincial Forestry Department, in command. Skipper Warburton sailed his craft to the regatta from Port Washington, Pender Island and before the start of the first race cruised among the anchored boats carrying two huge signs warning all within reading distance to beware of fire in the woods. The boat was additionally decorated with a number of green balsam trees." (Quoted from the *Nanaimo Free Press,* July 18th., 1923.)

Finally, on the cover of volume III, number 2, I found this:

OLIVER G. CLARK

"Choked and burnt in the fiery hell,
He rushed to the water's edge, and fell.
And in his hand, so tightly clasped,
We found his Badge of Service grasped.
His Forest Badge as if to say,
'I've done my duty' . . .

　　　　　　Far away
The night winds whisper over the tide,
'He did his duty — and he died.'
No nobler tribute could we give:
HE DIED THAT OTHER MEN MIGHT LIVE."

*　　*　　*　　*　　*　　*

And just for a moment I understood. I was immersed in the aura of the past which clung so pervasively to those pages. I understood the feelings of Clark's comrades, and the sincerity of the poet, and the real meaning of the words. Inside that issue there was a straightforward account of the incident:

"A fire had broken out on the day before near a logging camp and, after strenuous exertions, had been confined within narrow limits when the wind changed suddenly and carried the flames down towards a small settlement.

Port Neville, June 25, 1925 at 1.45 p.m.

"Assistant Ranger CLARK was engaged in organizing the women and children and sending them down to the Forest Service launch which was standing by. There was no time to spare as the fire swept down on the hamlet as the people were got out, but CLARK went back to search the houses in case any children might have been left behind in the rush for safety. Unfortunately he did not mention that he was doing so, and the boat pulled out of range before he was missed. As soon as possible, his companions went back in a small boat, and found his body near the landing.

"CLARK was a veteran of the Great War and was looked upon as a thoroughly efficient officer of the Provincial Forest Service."

* * * * * *

And so on Tuesday, November 3rd., 1925, the Premier, John Oliver, unveiled an illuminated scroll to the memory of Clark. In his address the Premier paid tribute to Clark's courage; and the memorial scroll, together with a portrait of Clark, was placed prominently in the Provincial Library. "There to remain," the Premier said, "so long as these buildings shall stand."

Or at least until the place was renovated. The scroll read as follows:

"TO THE MEMORY OF OLIVER GOSNOLD CLARK
Ranger, B. C. Forest Service,
who lost his life in the noble discharge of his duty on the twenty-fifth day
of June, 1925, at Port Neville.

. . . . . .

A fire, of which he had charge, was whipped beyond control by a sudden change of wind, leaving only a few minutes for escape. Ignoring his own danger, Clark carried the warning to his crews and saw them safely to rafts and boats in the bay. He returned to the logging camp to make sure that no one had been missed. His body was subsequently found by his comrades, his Forest Service badge tightly clasped in his lifeless hand, bearing mute testimony that under the supreme test he had magnificently conceived and nobly discharged his duty. Ranger Clark has gone, but has left us an inspiring example of courage and devotion to duty which will persist until the last Forest Fire is conquered and completely out."

* * * * * *

It is perhaps the intrusion of terrible facts into the romance and idealism of that era which results in the stumbling reaction of the writers of the day. It was as though the horrible death of Clark had to be woven into the tapestry of the times, to take its place among the fantasy of primeval forests and surging ocean, and stern men going inflexibly about their duty, never shirking, giving their all, sleeping without blankets.

In less than five months after his death Oliver Clark had become slightly unreal, almost mythical. I want to *know* Clark, to *feel* for him, the way I knew and felt for Campbell when he put the torch to the *Leila R*. But I can't. I can't get at the real man; he's all dressed up in legend like gift wrapping. I find myself giving inordinate attention to one single nonsense question: Did Clark *really* die with his badge in his hand?

Five years later.
Douglas Fir, Cottonwood *and* Oliver Clark *at Thurston Bay in* 1930

Back to reality. Heroes can be a problem, because they tend to create villains. And some time back there in 1925 a nasty whisper began to rustle through the bush. 'Root and Branch' stomped on it, fast.

"... we wish to call attention to an unfortunate misunderstanding, for which we ourselves have possibly but all unwittingly been partly to blame. Naturally the first reports of this distressing affair were somewhat incomplete and disjointed, and the impression seems to be current that Clark's comrades left him to his fate. Nothing could be further from the truth. Supervisor J. Thompson and Engineer Haley who were upon the Forest Branch launch, clung for hours to the outskirts of that raging inferno at the imminent risk of their own lives, in the vain hope of saving Clark. Time and time again their craft was actually afire, but still they stayed until all hope of rescuing Clark had fled and they were able to rescue only his body. Then, and not until then, did they leave the spot."

So at the end of 1925 they named a boat after him.

"I christen this vessel the *Oliver Clark* and may she prove as staunch and true in the service as the valiant man whose name she bears." Thus said Miss Doris Pattullo, daughter of the Premier. The vessel measured forty feet long with a nine foot six inch beam and a Vivian 16 h.p. heavy duty engine. She was built by Rodd Brothers in Victoria.

And finally, realism in the person of Wilf Archer, ex-Ranger, sitting in his office at Campbell River in 1981, bluff and forthright:

"Sure, I ran the old *Oliver Clark* for a couple of years. She was a long, skinny double-ender and by then she had a six-cylinder Chrysler gas engine. The engine was right in the back of the boat and the wheelhouse was right in front. In between you had the living quarters and the galley, and you ran her single-handed. To get back to the engine you had to gallop all the full length of the boat. It didn't seem to matter how good a condition she was in; when you came in for a landing either your throttle would stick or your clutch cord would break, and you'd have to go running for that bloody engine and throw it out of gear . . . Aaargh, she was a right bastard."

The new navy needed a base. There was fuel to be stored, there were repairs to be carried out. And so in 1913 a depot was set up at Heriot Bay, consisting of a float and a two-roomed shack. The weather was vile and misgivings were voiced during that first winter, as the ocean heaved into the bay and squalls swept through the trees. Was this bleak spot to be the capital of the new empire?

In the spring of the following year they decided to search for a better site. In an age without satellite photographs and oceanographic surveys, two hardy men by the names of Benedict and Black took the *R. J. Skinner* on a week's cruise, and looked around.

They found Thurston Bay, on Sonora Island.

Today Thurston Bay looks much the same as it must have done that day in 1914, when the *R. J. Skinner* nosed round the point and its crew sighted the promised land. Today there is no sign of the buildings and the ships' ways, no memory of the Rangers and the carpenters and the engineers, or of their families who lived and worked and laughed and quarrelled in the loneliness and privation of their island outpost. The grass has grown back and the sea has scoured the signs of men from the beach, and even the boats are long since gone, several of which wetted their planks for the first time in Thurston Bay. The bush has moved in now, and the only sign of the old station is the remains of the Pelton wheel which once supplied electricity.

Then, as now, Thurston Bay was wild and beautiful, and visitors used to comment on this, and tell the inhabitants how lucky they were.

"Visitors didn't have to live there," Hank Doerksen told me, cryptically. Hank, now Director of Protection Branch, describes his early experiences at Thurston Bay in a later chapter.

So they started construction under the supervision of Ranger McConnell — Rangers being jacks of all trades in those days. They built ways and boat storage, floats, houses and a bunkhouse. In 1917 they laid the keel for their first home-built boat, the *Sitka Spruce*. At that time the permanent staff numbered six: the Supervisor, his clerk, the Station Foreman, the Head Mechanic, the Head Boatbuilder, and the Radio Operator.

"... their first home-built boat, the Sitka Spruce.*"*

The 'Root and Branch' for November 1922 makes light of the lot of these men.

> "The location is extremely picturesque, its chief disability from a social standpoint being that it is somewhat isolated from the main current of human affairs. But even that has now been mitigated to a great extent since the installation of the Radio set . . . "

Building and repair work proceeded apace. The *Red Cedar* and *Douglas Fir* were built in 1918, thirty-two foot sisterships to the *Sitka Spruce*. They now had the means to tailor the older boats to suit the job, and rebuilding began with the *Eunice B* in 1918, continuing with the *Eva R* in 1919 and the *Kiora*, *Euclataw* and *Geraldine R* in 1921.

Then, in 1923, the Station undertook its most ambitious project to date: the construction of a fifty-seven foot Headquarters launch, the *B.C. Forester*. She was laid out by Wally Gilmour, the Chief Shipwright, launched in 1924 and completed in Vancouver.

In her original form she was a solid, square-set craft with accommodation for eleven, featuring generous headroom in the chart-house, with a separate engineroom and main cabin. Aft is the galley, and headroom here looks a little

restricted for Al, the cook; but in the words of the 'Root and Branch,' "Al doesn't need a lot of headroom anyway." Men and boats formed permanent bonds in those days, like men and horses. It didn't occur to the 'Root and Branch' that Al might take it into his head to quit, to be replaced by a seven-foot Swede.

There was a brief report on her initial trials, too. "She answers to the helm with a readiness which is almost disconcerting, and we noticed she displayed no tendency to roll in the wash from the S. S. *Solduc*."

The report continues in tones of proper awe: "We are not familiar with the principle on which the Diesel engine operates, but we know that it has been thoroughly established and is abundantly successful." With a wealth of good omens the *B. C. Forester* went into service.

She worked hard and well, apparently. In 1935 they decided to lengthen her, and she returned to her birthplace at Thurston Bay. Tommy Edwards told me the story.

"They put six feet on the forward end; they cut her back and scarfed it in. By that time Wally Gilmour had been succeeded by McCrae. They had an old tongue-and-groove floor at Thurston Bay, and when McCrae laid out the extension he was able to pick out the old lines still on the floor, from the original layout in 1923."

The *B. C. Forester* held a dark secret. "When they were stripping the planks back to tie the new section in," Tommy continued, "they found broken frames in the engine room. They wondered how the devil those frames could have got broken — she was a well-built ship and it must have taken quite a wallop to do that.

"It turned out she'd gone aground one time and I guess they shored her up to keep her upright when the tide went out, but they did a poor job of it, and she crashed over on her side. There were three people on the boat, and they agreed never to tell."

We can visualize the trio of conspirators, huddled at midnight on some remote sandbar beside their stranded craft, swearing their dark and dreadful oath. "I wish people wouldn't do that," John Paynter said plaintively. "If they told us exactly what happened when they have an accident, we wouldn't have to spend time looking for other problems. But people seem so deathly scared to tell, in case they lose their jobs. It's a sickness which seems to run through all large organizations."

But there are exceptions, and none more delightful than this gem from the 'Root and Branch,' August 1922:

"Asst Ranger R. A. Beattie (Whaletown), while in charge of the launch *Birch*, and towing a dinghy, attempted to cross the bows of a fishing craft, with the result that the dinghy was stove-in and lost. Beattie did not await the findings of the Tribunal, but promptly handed in his resignation. In other words, Beattie beat it. 'Thus conscience doth make cowards of us all!'"

* * * * * *

In 1924 the *Check Scaler* was built; an assistant Ranger launch of thirty feet, very similar in appearance to five boats bought from Hoffar's around 1921 — the first Blimps, described in the next chapter. In the same year the *Chestnut* emerged, a small twenty-five footer.

Two years later the *Sonora* slid down the ways, a speedy twenty-nine footer with a large after cockpit, a tiny wheelhouse and a long foredeck, for use on lakes. And finally in 1929 the *Cypress II* appeared, about the same size as the *Chestnut*. Then operations were curtailed for the duration of the Depression and maintenance work only was undertaken. Use of the boats was cut down too; assistant Ranger launches only went out during the summer months.

Eventually, in the late Thirties, it became clear that the days of Thurston Bay as a maintenance and boat building depot were numbered. It was a long way from the source of supply, skilled men were hard to find, and when World War II came along the coastal shipyards were so busy with military orders that they didn't have time to attend to other needs. The steamship service up the coast had begun to dwindle, further isolating Thurston Bay, and finally the decision was taken to move to the present site of the Depot on the Fraser. By that time there were about six men left at the Thurston Bay marine station, with Bob Swan in charge and Grant Allen overseeing the boatbuilding. The old buildings were propped up with poles and the plant generally was showing signs of decay.

So in 1941 everything of value was removed and they put Thurston Bay shops to the torch, sparing the nearby Ranger Station with its buildings and staff.

* * * * * *

"They put Thurston Bay shops to the torch."

"The new boat repair plant on the Fraser River is just about completed," ran the Newsletter item in July 1941. "It is a fine, well-built and well-planned piece of construction that rivals anything on the coast."

The ashes of Thurston Bay were barely cold before the new plant was in operation and three boats on the ways for overhaul: the *Nesika*, the skinny *Oliver Clark*, and the *A. L. Bryant*, a ship of ill-omen.

The new Marine Station was indeed an impressive complex.

Situated on Celtic Avenue it was built by Ward and Sons of New Westminster, under the watchful eye of the Forest Service Mechanical Superintendent, Jim Blake. The Station was taken over on July 11th., 1941 at a brief ceremony attended by the Honourable A. Wells Gray, Minister of Lands.

The Station consisted of a large building 132 feet long by 100 feet wide, with machine shop, carpenters' shop, two boat ways, stockroom and offices. Much of the machinery came from Thurston Bay. Later in the year construction began on a second floor, which was to house a pump and outboard motor shop.

Pumps loom large in the world of the Forest Service, as they are perhaps the most important tool in fighting forest fires. The earliest fire-fighting pumps were built by Fairbanks-Morse and Evinrude. These had their problems and in due course the Forest Service came out with their own design under the guidance of C. S. Cowan, then Forester in charge of Protection.

With the naive optimism of the day they named it the 'Wonder' and, since it weighed 255 lbs., they described it as 'portable.' A later description betrays dis-illusionment: "It took two men and a boy anywhere from five minutes to five hours to get it started, but once started it went,' And go it did, apparently. Suffering from uncontrollable vibration it had a tendency to go jittering off through the bush like a spastic moose.

"We are not belittling the 'Wonder' pump," they were saying by 1941. "It did, in its day, pump an ocean of water on a lot of fires." But by then some-thing better had come along: the pump of Jim McDonald. To this was added the genius of one Max Bennett; and the result was the last word in pumps— the Bennett-McDonald pump, using a chainsaw motor and a large proportion of magnesium in its construction.

Bob Swan was in charge in those early days. They didn't have the protective piling around the Fraser dock then, and stray logs with heavy butts would jam under the wharves at high tide. As the tide ebbed the butt would dig into the mud and by low tide the wharf would be propped up six feet clear of the water. So Bob would always watch the wharves closely during the falling tide, and at the first sign of levitation he'd take a line from the winch of a Cat on shore, slip it around the log and winch it clear.

Or so the theory went.

One fine morning a wharf began to rear into the air and Bob came rumbling up on the Cat. The line was attached, the winch started up and Bob stepped down to supervise. The line tightened and the Cat's voice deepened as the winch began to labour. The log was jammed solidly against the riverbed. The men watched stoically. Then the Cat's engine began to run a little more easily although, oddly enough, the log didn't seem to be moving.

The Cat was, however. Bob had forgotten to apply the brake. Drawn forward by its own winch it scuttled across the bank like a charging crocodile, tilted, and plunged into the Fraser, narrowly missing the *Maple* which was tied up nearby.

Tommy Edwards related this incident to me, and like the drowned Cat in Lake Williston, it reflected very much to the credit of the men.

"We got a crane in and we pulled the Cat out next morning, and by noon we had it operating. That's how efficient the old plant was, by gosh. I doubt whether they'd be able to do that today," said Tommy.

After Bob Swan came Jim McDonald, a tall forester with a Scots brogue, well remembered for the time he stormed the citadel of the District Office and fought a desk-thumping battle with the District Forester over the vexed problem of injectors for the *Syrene*, and who should pay for them. "But they shook hands afterwards," Tommy told me. "They were big men in those days."

In 1952 the round-faced Harry Hill took over, a man who had served his time in sailing ships; very knowledgeable about boat operations. Harry ran a tight ship. He was not averse to issuing brusque orders to his superiors if occasion demanded it—like a celebrated occasion when the fast planing Ranger launch *Western Hemlock* was being delivered to Prince Rupert. She accomplished the trip at an average running speed of 20.5 knots—probably establishing a record for small craft. Harry was in charge; and Bob Swan, Tommy Edwards and John Paynter were there. Also on board was the retiring Deputy Minister on his way to say his farewells to the staff at Prince Rupert.

By evening they were tied up to a log boom at the northern tip of Vancouver Island. After dinner the Deputy Minister produced a bottle of whiskey and invited the crew to join him in a drink.

Harry stood there bristling, hands on hips. "Now look here, sir, I need these boys to be up and going at five o'clock in the morning!"

The Deputy Minister blinked at him owlishly. "Just one little drink each, then."

Harry relented. After all, the Old Man *was* retiring. "All right. Just one. Make it a small one."

So the company downed their tot and turned in, leaving the Deputy Minister contemplating his bottle.

In the morning the *Western Hemlock* leaped into action and raced across the Pacific rollers. Tommy Edwards was at the controls. Walls of water smashed into the bows—immediately behind which lay the Deputy Minister, curled up in the fo'c'sle. He seemed overtired so they didn't disturb him, and the boat had covered over a hundred miles before he climbed into the wheelhouse, rubbing red-rimmed eyes and wilting before the reproving gaze of Harry Hill.

Just once Harry lost his dignity. One day at the Marine Station a small boat with a flared bow lay at the dock. It was intended that it should be powered by a large outboard motor, but this had not been installed.

Harry Hill, hands on hips, was directing some operations across the other side of the storage basin. Matters were not meeting with his approval. His cherubic face was flushed with annoyance and he began to shout. In order to get a better vantage point he stepped forward onto the wide bow of the little boat.

But Harry Hill, master mariner, had forgotten that the little boat's engine had not been fitted.

Lacking any counterbalancing weight in the stern, the boat tilted. Soon the murky waters of the Fraser closed over Harry's head in full sight of the men, who had to be sure they got all their laughing done before he surfaced. When he reappeared it was with all his usual aplomb, his hat still firmly on his head, to be helped from the water by anxious and serious-faced employees.

Harry's successor in 1964 was Arnold Bjorndahl, a Norwegian and an ex-R.C.A.F. Squadron Leader. Lacking experience in boat-building and maintenance, Arnold relied heavily on Tommy Edwards and others for advice. After Arnold died in 1968, Tommy took over.

* * * * * *

"The new Marine Station was indeed an impressive complex."

Tommy was enjoying his retirement when I called to see him at his home in a quiet Vancouver street. Tall and smiling, he was eager to talk about the Marine Station and the boats, but first I needed some personal information.

"We're a seafaring family," he said. "We go back to the days of Captain Bligh. My great-great-great grandfather was Edward Edwards, in command of the British frigate *Pandora*. My great-great grandfather captained the first steamship to run from Swansea to Liverpool. My great grandfather was a captain as well, but he died at the age of 27 — he's buried in the banks of the St. Lawrence.

"But my grandfather was the most colorful of them all. He was skipper of the *Illyrian*, which held the Blue Riband of the Atlantic. He got a citation for saving the crew of the *Isaac Webb*. At that time of the Russo-Turkish war he ran the Russian blockade through the Dardanelles — he got a medal for that..." He went into the basement, returning with small boxes containing medals. The Turkish medal was exceptionally beautiful; a many-pointed star.

"Then he acquired a ship of his own — the *Manauense*. In 1898 he took an expedition out of Britain and guaranteed he'd put them in Dawson City without setting foot on land in between. My father was on that ship; he was thirteen at the time. My grandfather had a sternwheeler built here by Wallace who later owned Burrard Shipyard. He brought some steam barges from Britain and he towed this sternwheeler, the *James Donville*, to the mouth of the Yukon at St. Michael, Alaska, and they steamed right up the river to Dawson City."

He sighed. "He lost all his money on that venture. His cousin was writing cheques that he didn't know about..."

Tommy's father served his time on sailing ships, then spent the rest of his life towboating off the coast of B.C. until he died in 1940. Tommy himself, like his grandfather, suffered the heartbreak of business failure — again through no fault of his own — before signing on as a boatbuilder at Thurston Bay on April 3rd, 1939. In the fall of 1941 he became head boatbuilder, and by 1946 he was foreman of the new Forest Service Marine Station. In 1965 he became Assistant Superintendent, and in 1968 he succeeded Arnold Bjorndahl as Superintendent.

"In all the time I was at the Marine Station we built well over a hundred boats," he told me. "The bigger ones were the *Tachi III* in 1950, the *Forest Ranger II* in 1953, the *Forest Supervisor* in 1956, and the *Pacific Yew* right after. Then there was the *Yellow Pine*, the *Western Hemlock* in 1958, the

"We rebuilt the Wells Gray."

Forest Dispatcher in 1961 — those last two were sisters. Then the biggest: the *Coast Ranger* in 1968. In between we rebuilt boats: the *Wells Gray*, the *B.C. Forester*, the *White Cloud*, the *Oliver Clark II*. And we built eleven Blimps."

He went on to speak of the long, narrow riverboats; and others, the ones they bought, refitted to Forest Service standards, and sent up the coast. Exciting incidents: the loss of the *A. L. Bryant*, and the time the *Pacific Yew* sank at the dock.

And the time the Marine Station caught fire.

*　*　*　*　*　*

In the small hours of May 17th., 1949, Jim McDonald was in hospital recovering from a kidney operation and Tommy Edwards, the foreman, was sleeping the sleep of the healthy and blameless in his own bed. At half-past three he was jolted awake by the telephone. It was the watchman from the Marine Station. His tone was urgent.

"Tommy! There's smoke coming out of the stockroom!"

"Did you call the Fire Department?"

"Yes."

"Hold on. I'm coming," said Tommy. He dressed, jumped into his car and drove fast.

Meanwhile the police, having intercepted the watchman's call to the Fire Department, had arrived at the Marine Station. The watchman showed them the stockroom with smoke oozing from beneath the door.

"Well, now," said a policeman with more courage than sense, "we'd better take a look."

And he kicked the door in.

The air rushed in and the room burst into flames. As the men backed off, the fire roared past them, straight up the stairwell into the loft. There sat a number of Bennett-McDonald pumps in varying stages of assembly, rich in magnesium. As the flames licked around them they began to explode like incendiary bombs...

Fifteen minutes after receiving the watchman's call, Tommy Edwards reached the top of a rise and saw a glow against the night clouds. As he drove on the Marine Station came into view, flames bursting through the roof and reaching into the sky. He found the fire trucks already there. One was hooked up to the only hydrant, another was trying without much success to suck water from the river, and a third was bogged down in loose sand. It was not a scene to inspire confidence, and as Tommy ran around towards the riverside he drew some consolation from the fact that the beautiful *Syrene* was moored safely outside. The ways had been set up to receive her the following day.

But there were two Blimps in the carpenters' shop: the *Arbutus II* and the *Alder II*. And on the east ways lay the *Larch II*, newly built by C. H. Hudson and Co., her paint already beginning to blister and smoke.

Tommy climbed the slope of the ways. Far above him, flames were running along the roof trusses; and closer, the fire was beginning to take hold of the lumber in the carpenters' shop. Tommy reached the bows of the *Larch II* but could get no further; the winch at the head of the ways was engulfed in flames. Running outside, he borrowed an axe and returned to the *Larch II*. He swung at the cable which ran from the bows to the winch. The keen edge of the blade doubled over with the force of his blow, but the cable did not part. Frustrated, Tommy threw the axe aside. Cinders rained down from the roof and lay smouldering around him.

"We had our moments of excitement."

Then he noticed that his efforts had had some effect. The cable was hanging less tautly. With the heat searing his skin, he struggled to remove the pin from the block and, after a few seconds, it came free. Tommy threw his weight against the *Larch II*. She shifted, then began to roll. Accelerating, she ploughed into the water outside, dug up a cloud of spray, and scooted across the Fraser. Tommy ran for safety.

Eventually the fire was brought under control and the *Arbutus II* and *Alder II* were saved. Subsequent investigation proved the fire to have been electrical in origin. Part of the walls remained standing, but most of the roof had to be replaced.

"We had our moments of excitement," Tommy said.

*   *   *   *   *   *

By 1965 the Marine Station had diversified into other areas and was renamed the Forest Service Maintenance Depot. A number of specialized items were built that were not generally available on the market. Under the guidance of Max Bennett they began to manufacture hose couplings, valves and other forest protection equipment.

In the last ten years the emphasis has shifted to reforestation. The Depot has developed equipment for bundling and packing seedlings, and other specialized equipment used in modern nursery seedling production. Wally McDonald is in charge today.

John Paynter summed it up.

"There was an interesting progression," he told me, "from tinkering with things like pumps and outboard motors, to being involved with them — eventually to the point where we became authorities on some of them. Max Bennett, for example, was looked on as *the* authority on pumps. Industry used to come to him."

A far cry from the early days, when the *R. J. Skinner* rounded the headland and Benedict and Black first saw Thurston Bay.

THE BLIMPS

There were eleven of them. They were thirty-two feet long, nine feet wide and four feet deep. They were sturdy no-nonsense vessels built of fir and cedar. They were known officially as Assistant Ranger launches.

They were known lovingly as Blimps.

How did the name come about?

We have to look back to the early days, when people realized that a secondary type of boat was needed; a boat less than the lordly Ranger launch, yet more than a runabout. What was needed, was a one-man boat with seaworthy characteristics, able to go wherever the work took the man, able to shelter him overnight.

In 1921 the Forest Branch took delivery of five boats from Hoffar Brothers of Vancouver: the *Alder*, *Arbutus*, *Balsam*, *Cherry* and *Oak*. They were each thirty feet long, with an eight foot beam and a two foot nine draft. Their original engine was a Vivian 8 h. p. Their maximum speed was around seven knots, and they were the Forest Branch's first Assistant Ranger launches. A similar boat, the *Birch*, was built about the same time, probably by V. M. Dafoe of Vancouver. She can be seen alongside *Alder* in an early photograph of Thurston Bay, but her statistics are lost in antiquity.

In appearance these boats were tidy and workmanlike although there seems to have been some difficulty in achieving headroom without giving the boat a top-heavy look. The wheelhouse is slightly taller than aesthetics demand, and the cabin has a markedly cambered roof.

This tends to give the after end of the boat a bloated look, like a dog long drowned. It prompted one Ranger, back in the Twenties, to remark:

"She looks like a bloody great blimp."

The resemblance to the wartime non-rigid airship is not particularly apt, but the name stuck.

*　*　*　*　*　*

In 1924 the six became seven, with the building of the *Check Scaler* at Thurston Bay. Her dimensions were similar to Hoffar's boats; she also had the Vivian 8 h. p. engine, and in appearance was much the same although the wheelhouse was slightly lower. The cambered cabin roof was retained.

　　　　　　　"Little is known of the career of the Check Scaler.*"*

The Blimps

Little is known of the career of the *Check Scaler*, although Frank Tannock had some choice comments on her which could probably be extended to the other ships of this particular lineage. By this time she had been re-engined.

"She was a real dandy. She had a two-cylinder Gardner right there in the wheelhouse. You practically sat on it. Stink, diesel oil all over the place. She did all of six knots. She was used out of Alert Bay, in my time. I ran into grief with her in Malaspina Straits between Texada Island and the mainland. The engine quit on me. The fuel filter was plugged with sludge—it was always happening. As if it wasn't enough to spend hours in the wheelhouse with the engine banging away beside you. Boy, if she didn't give you a headache, there was something wrong with you."

So much for the affection of a man for his boat.

Back to the original six.

Although intended for summer use, the new Blimps caught the eye of other agencies who coveted them for off-season purposes. One was lent to the Attorney-General's department in the winter of 1922 to help enforce the Game Laws. "And we are pleased to assist our good friends the Provincial Police,"

"The cabin has a markedly cambered roof."

enthused 'Root and Branch'. " . . . the *Alder* will go to Pender Harbour."

Alas for co-operation. A terse item in February 1923 states: "The Provincial Police have reported to us the destruction by fire of the launch *Alder* at Powell River last week. No details are yet to hand." Obviously possessed of dire forebodings, the writer continues, "It will be remembered that the *Alder* was one of the three launches loaned by the Forest Branch to the Provincial Police to assist the latter in their work this winter. The others were the *Douglas Fir* and the *Birch*." *And where are they now?* he seems to be asking.

Happily they were alive and well, and even the report of *Alder's* destruction was exaggerated. The smoking hulk was rebuilt and put back into service, and as late as 1936 her log contained the following inspirational passage:

"July 2. 0830: left Ganges. 1230: 2 miles off north end of Porlier Pass, engine stopped; found cylinder head filled with water, the wall being corroded. Got into dinghy and pulled 2 miles to nearest telephone on Galiano Island. Phoned to Corporal D. O. Tweedhope at Ganges, Saltspring Island. Reported position and condition, advising that immediate towing to shelter was necessary to save launch from piling up on a lee shore. Returned to launch in dinghy. Velocity of wind had increased,

"In 1953 they butchered the Arbutus."

position now ½ mile from shore. Detached anchor and chain from *Alder* and fastened to bow of dinghy. Assembled all available rope, made one end fast to stern of dinghy and the other to bow of launch. Let go anchor and submerged dinghy. This improvised sea anchor held head of launch up to wind, and retarded drift considerably. 1630: Picked up by P. M. L. 6, Corporal Tweedhope in charge. Lifted anchor and recovered dinghy. 1900: Arrived Ganges, in tow. Signed: W. E. Jansen, Assistant Ranger."

The *Alder* sailed on, and it was not until 1947 that she was finally sold to W. P. Haggerty of Vancouver.

In 1953 they butchered the *Arbutus*. The Pacific Great Eastern right-of-way along the shores of Howe Sound needed clearing, and a boat was required for carrying men and equipment on the job. The *Arbutus*, earmarked for sale after a quiet life in service, was reprieved and converted by removing the cabin. This gave her a commodious open well aft of the wheelhouse.

She was renamed *Elco* in anticipation of her sale in 1955. It was common practice to rename boats before sale so that the fund of available tree names was not depleted to the extent that an M. V. *Cascara* became a necessity. John Paynter didn't bestow the non-forest names; this reponsibility was assumed by his boss, Howard Taylor. I asked Howard where he got the names from; in

addition to *Elco* there had been *Burwick*, *Betty Harris*, *Gleam*, *Joseph*, *Zoe* and many others.

"Christ, I don't know," he said, leaving me to understand that they'd welled up from his subconscious, connected in some Freudian way with traumatic experiences from his childhood.

The *Oak* was sold in 1949. No details are available of the career of the *Balsam*, but the *Cherry* was mentioned in dispatches from time to time. You will recall that this was the boat which the redoubtable Ranger Gritten had piled onto the rocks near Pender.

Surprisingly, one of her log books is still in existence. The following entry is dated July 10th., 1922.

"10.25. Struck rock off Clough's Ranch, tide falling launch fast by stern, all efforts to move of no avail.
"11.00. Launch took heavy list to starboard, filling rapidly, Clough's launch alongside, boat too full of water to do anything, stern resting easily on rock, bows under water.
"12.00. Ranger Gritten left in Clough's launch to secure assistance in re-floating.
"13.00. Launch *Yamasan* and *R. J. Skinner* alongside, lines passed from boat to boat under launch, tide rising, launch floating.
"16.00. Boat *Yamasan* left. *R. J. Skinner* took launch in tow."

Gritten could give as good as he took, however, and an entry on October 24th. of the same year notes: "Helped to salvage Bromfield & Co.'s launch. Also assisted in the salvage of a yacht."

On January 11th., 1924 Ranger Sweatman took over, and the log contains the following irascible note:

"Engine developed trouble 1 hr. out from Thurston Bay. Stopped and took off cyl. head. Salt under seat of intake valve. Replaced head and proceeded. Developed same trouble shortly afterwards. Made Chanet Bay. Took off cyl. head and tested head for leak also water jacket; practically all water in base. Drained base and replaced with fresh oil. Everything apparently O. K. Note: I would suggest that the parties responsible for the upkeep of engines at Thurston Bay would make sure that the machinery aboard the boats under their care were inspected more closely before they send them out as being 'mechanically perfect.'"

Then, on April 27th., 1924, the *Cherry* got a new master.

"Took over launch *Cherry* at Thurston Bay and proceeded to Beaver Creek to meet Ranger E. P. Burchett." (signed) Oliver G. Clark.

Uncle Oliver's trail was still warm. In untidy handwriting he recorded the voyages of *Cherry* (May 17th. Picked up launch *Kiora* with broken steering gear and towed her to Reid Bay) until May 31st., 1924.

Then nothing more.

His last entry on that date read, "No run. Weather fair, wind W. light. O. G. Clark."

And on the next line, just the date: "June 1st."

Put in new igmythles & cleaned Launch
Weather Rain 2 hrs (heavy) Wind SE strong
O.G. Clark

29d No run
Weather Rain 4 hrs heavy Wind S.E. light

30th

L. Beaver Creek 7.30
Arr. Greys Creek 8.30
Leave " 10.20
Arr. Beaver Creek 14.05 O G Clark

162

May 31st No run
Weather Fair, Wind W. light.
O G Clark

June 1st

Of the period between June 1st. and June 25th., when he died, there was nothing. Just an empty page followed by the first entry of D. New, who took over on July 1st. No last words, no descriptions of the fire, no premonitions of death. The trail was cold again.

*   *   *   *   *   *

The *Cherry* was plagued by engine problems. "It seems inconceivable that this engine was thoroughly overhauled at Thurston Bay," wrote Allan McClean. And "Flopped around for about an hour trying to get engine started without result. Rigged sail from blanket..." ran the log of E. J. Gregory. But the *Cherry's* most exciting moments came during the War, when she saw action in Johnstone Strait, being fired upon by the military base at York Island. Finally in 1942, a sad note in the Newsletter:

"Our fleet suffered a blow in the wrecking of the launch *Cherry*, which was crushed by a crib of poles breaking away during flood water at Campbell River in November. While the *Cherry* was salvaged, her rejuvenation will practically amount to building a new launch."

Whether they did rebuild her is not known; but the days of her class were already numbered. They were getting old and they were uncomfortable boats by the improving standards of the day. Tommy Edwards spoke of them briefly but pungently:

"I came down from Thurston Bay in one of those. We hit a south-easter coming through Welcome Pass and had green curling right up round the windows there. It was coming down the stovepipe and I was lucky I had somebody with me, because he was holding the battery on. It was an old Palmer two-cylinder engine and if the battery had jumped off with all that pitching and tossing, we wouldn't have had any ignition."

In 1943 the first of a new breed appeared.

*   *   *   *   *   *

The Newsletter for September of that year carried the following item written with all the fond enthusiasm of a birth announcement:

"Accompanying photos are of the new *Red Cedar II* 'Blimp' one-man patrol launch, 34 feet long, 9 foot beam, built from scratch, or keel, at

"In 1943 the first of a new breed appeared."

the Forest Service Fraser River plant, from plans prepared by A. E. Thompson, chief draughtsman, Victoria; and launched in July. Bob Swan, Plant foreman, his crew, Thompson, Jimmy Blake and District Officers, to say nothing of the Chief, are all very proud of the *Red Cedar*. It is undoubtedly the finest of its type to date by reason of design and fine workmanship. The *Red Cedar* should warm the heart of some patrolman for many years to come."

The photographs showed a trim craft with a short foredeck and forward wheelhouse, with engineroom immediately behind, followed by a cabin and small after deck, with a square stern. She was not dissimilar from the old *Kiora*, although her bluff bows and straight stem gave her a more pugnacious look.

It is possible that the Newsletter's enthusiasm was misplaced. Years later, Frank Tannock said, "I was Ranger in Port Alberni with the *Red Cedar II*. It had a two-cylinder Gardner and it did a sizzling six knots. And I had all of Alberni Inlet and Barkley Sound to do. A trip down there would take ten days. And it had a wick-burning stove that was very temperamental; you never knew if your beans would be hot . . . Off Beale we met a real howling south-easter. Have you ever been in a submarine? That was the *Red Cedar* that day. Just green water right over her. The Blimps had a reputation for being wet boats. Helldivers, some people called them . . . "

What had gone wrong? I asked Tommy Edwards.

"*Red Cedar*? She wasn't a bad boat, but she seemed heavy in the water. Her transom was deep and she dragged her ass; she was no hell for speed. They were a little disappointed in her. So Jim McDonald and Charlie Haddon came to me and said, 'Tom, what can you do with that boat?' And I said, 'I'll start over again.'"

So Tommy went to work. His drawing instruments were somewhat unusual, consisting of a spline, a thin length of oak which he could bend, and a stay from a woman's corset. These deficiencies were offset by a wealth of experience and an instinctive understanding of boats.

He took the basic waterline length of the *Red Cedar II* and raked the stem, giving her an overall length of thirty-four feet seven inches. He shortened the shaft-logs to around three feet and gave her a good tuck. He raised the transom so that only two inches were wetted, at rest. Instead of the five and a half inch deadrise he gave her three and a half inches. He allowed the same basic beam, raised the sheer and was thereby able to lower the cabin. He planned

for a three-cylinder Jimmy engine. He made a half-model, the way he'd been trained.

"By gosh, I remember the day we launched her. They said, 'How the hell did you do it, Tommy? She's perfect!'"

That was the *Cherry II*, and she was launched on February 14th., 1946 by the Honourable E. T. Kenney, Minister of Lands and Forests.

As she lay in the water Tommy, listening to the praise of the spectators, was still not satisfied. "She was up a little bit in the stern. The water tank was under the wheelhouse floor too, and after fitting her out with controls I realized it would be better to get that tank out of there. So the next boat—the *Douglas Fir II* which we built in 1947—I moved the water tank ahead and made the section a bit fuller. All the rest were built like that.

"They were well-structured boats," Tommy told me. "Six inch frames amidships, eight inch centres. Inch and a quarter planking, fir keel, yellow cedar horntimbers, gum stem and sternpost, yellow cedar transom, mahogany superstructure. Planking below water was fir, red cedar above. Inch and a quarter decks. I always put beam centres a little closer; most people have fourteen inch centres but I went to twelve—it only took one more beam, and you don't get the leaking problems. They gave very little trouble over the years. That semi-elliptical wheelhouse is all mine. They wanted square corners, but I didn't.

"They never carried any ballast, and anybody who had one, they always swore what a good sea boat they were. Bordie Grant used to escort them round to the West Coast of the Island and he'd say: 'Boy, Tom, they're a great little boat!'"

He grinned at me sheepishly, he'd got carried away. "I always feel pretty proud of them, you know," he admitted.

In 1949 came the *Alder II* and the *Arbutus II*, and in 1950 the *Western Ash*, *White Birch* and *Silver Fir* took the water. The new boats proved themselves quickly, and the class expanded to eleven boats by 1952 with the addition of the *Oak II*, *Cottonwood II* and *Sitka Spruce II*.

As the photographs show, there was no unusual camber to the cabin roof, but people by now had become accustomed to referring to Assistant Ranger launches as Blimps and so the nickname was perpetuated.

*   *   *   *   *   *

"Her transom was deep and she dragged her ass."

"How the hell did you do it, Tommy?"

In service the new Blimps did everything that was asked of them. The *Red Cedar II* was probably the least popular of the class, and she was expensive, too. On one occasion the rudder cable jumped a pulley at the mouth of the Fraser, and the Assistant Ranger, unable to diagnose the problem, flagged a tugboat down which towed him to the Maintenance Depot. The Assistant Ranger's gratitude was insufficient reward for the tugboat skipper, who put in a salvage claim for one-third of the value of the Blimp.

She was disposed of in 1967; the first Blimp to be sold.

A constructive letter was written by L. E. Gower to the Vancouver District Forester after inspecting the *Cherry II*, suggesting insulation to cut down the noise level and confirming the complaint of Frank Tannock and others, "The boat is somewhat bow heavy. This results in a tendency to ship water over the forward deck very readily . . . No heat is available in the pilot house . . . A little office accommodation could be incorporated . . ."

Apart from being holed by a deadhead in 1972 the *Cherry II* enjoyed an uneventful life and was finally sold in 1978.

The *Douglas Fir II* spent most of her time on the inside waters of the southern coast. In 1949 she was involved in one of the most unusual incidents in the history of the Forest Service while operating out of Chatham Channel. I got this story from Louie Lorentsen, whom I visited while he was building his retirement home on Saltspring Island.

"I was heading up from Thurston Bay to Chatham Channel," said Louie. "I'd just lined up on Broken Islands to turn off into Chatham Channel; by then I'd been in Johnstone Strait for about half an hour."

Suddenly the *Douglas Fir II* heeled over.

"I figured here's some kind of tidal wave. I tried to correct her with the helm but she wouldn't come back up. The next thing, there was the most godawful thump. It threw me to the floor of the wheelhouse. When I got up, the deck was canted over and there was water on the other side of the windows. I figured I'd better get out and start swimming."

He crawled back through the engine room and the cabin, all the time aware of the strange motion of the boat, the huge rushing of water and a drumming sound. The *Douglas Fir II* was riding with her nose steeply down, but when Louie clawed his way out onto the stern, he was relieved to find at least this part of the boat above water. The Blimp was rushing forward in a giant rolling sea, faster than she'd ever moved in her life.

And beside Louie towered a cliff of metal.

"I was caught right in under the bow of a freighter. We must have been doing ten knots. I couldn't see the deck because of the flare of the bow, and I didn't think anyone up there could see me. I started hollering to attract attention. I began to get scared that we'd meet a boat coming the other way, and the wake might roll the *Douglas Fir II* right under the freighter. That would be the end."

At last the freighter began to slow. Somebody knew Louie was there—but the S. S. *Joel Chandler Harris* was a big ship, and took a long time to stop.

"They threw a line down and I passed it through the portholes of the stern cabin, because I figured once she got away from the freighter she'd fill up and sink. The side was smashed in and one bunk was sitting in the middle of the cabin." But the bows came up, no more water came in, the engine was still running and it looked as though the Blimp might stay afloat. Louie took the freighter's details for his accident report and told them to cut him loose.

"The starboard side was stove right in, aft of the engine room. I put the dinghy out because I thought that if those planks decided to pop back out again, she might go down awful fast, and I didn't want to waste time fiddling with the davits. So I drove her home like that. When I got home I scared my wife quite a bit. What I didn't know was, I'd cut my head at some time and there was blood all over my face..."

The Court of Enquiry apportioned the blame 75% against the *Joel Chandler Harris* and 25% against Louie. As was to happen in the case of the *A. L. Bryant* a couple of years later, the smaller ship in the process of being overtaken was deemed to be partly at fault.

"If you're alone in the boat it's impossible to keep a proper lookout astern. You're watching the water ahead all the time, for deadheads and such," said Louie. "You pick out a point and head for it, and every once in a while you look behind, but most of the time you're looking ahead. I'd looked behind just after I'd passed Salmon River and seen nothing. It was a calm day, with perfect visibility. I think they were changing watches on the freighter and somehow they missed me.

"But they said they did see me," concluded Louie bitterly, "and they said I was wandering all over the Strait. I can't buy that. I've been on boats all my life."

*   *   *   *   *   *

The *Alder II* also became famous for a curious incident; this time in 1956. Her engine was overheating badly and her skipper, Assistant Ranger Don Trickett, had been trying to rig up a fresh-water cooling system, but to no avail. There was a south-easter blowing and he was drifting down on Harwood Island, off Powell River. He'd contacted the R. C. M. P. but they'd told him it would take them at least an hour to reach him. The situation was desperate.

Russ Campbell takes up the story. "I was flying up coast with Roy Moulton in a Beaver, and we overheard Don talking to Lund Ranger station. He seemed kind of upset — he was drifting onto the shoals. So we called him and asked if we could help, but he figured there wasn't much we could do, with an airplane.

66

"Roy put us down, though, and we threw *Alder* a line. I thought we might be able to hold her off the rocks until the R. C. M. P. arrived.

"So we started to pull a little bit—and gee, soon we were chugging along. We were up to five knots. So we kept going—why not? In the end we towed him right across the Straits. We'd reached the breakwater at Powell River before the R. C. M. P. came out to take him..."

Russ detected skepticism on my face. "Nobody believes that story—a float-plane towing a Blimp. It's true, though. I've got a photograph to prove it." And he had, too. It really happened.

* * * * * *

Like the *Alder II*, the *Arbutus II* was involved in the disastrous fire of 1949 at the Marine Station, but the damage was slight. Thereafter she performed her duties in the Vancouver District without undue incident, and was eventually transferred to the Corrections Branch in 1968. The *Alder II* spent most of her life at Lund and Thurston Bay before being sold in 1978 to Pryce Management Ltd. of Vancouver. The *Western Ash* also spent her time in the Vancouver District. In 1955 she suffered minor damage from a fire on board, and in 1968 she ran onto a rock. Again the damage was slight, and she worked on the inside waters until 1977, when she was sold to West Coast Salvage. The *White Birch*, built in the same year, lasted twenty-eight years in the Prince Rupert District before being sold to Bob Irving of Tofino in 1978. The *Silver Fir*, built in 1950, operated around Lund for many years before being sent overland to the Peace River country in 1965 together with the *Cherry II* to assist in the clearing work on Williston Lake. The *Oak II*, fitted with the engine from the ill-fated *A. L. Bryant*, worked in and around Campbell River until being disposed of in 1977 to West Coast Salvage.

It is a tribute to the design of the Blimps, and to the care of their operators, that their lives were relatively uneventful. It comes as quite a surprise to read of a minor incident in the life of the *Cottonwood II*, operating out of Tofino at the time:

"May 25, 1959. Launch proceeding from Tahsis to Esperanza Inlet. Boat suddenly lost way. Assisted by fishing vessel *Wenusk* to Esperanza hospital float, secured at float at 10.03 hours. Asst/Rgr Doerksen contacted Vancouver and advised them propeller apparently lost. He stated he had not felt anything, only heard a slight 'clunk,' apparently as a result of the propeller striking the shoe as it dropped away."

"May 26. *Yellow Cedar* left Esperanza with *Cottonwood II* in tow. Arrived Muir's boat works at Tahsis at 9.15 hours. Launch hauled up on ways at 16.45 hours. Shaft broken approximately 1½" aft of stern bearing and propeller gone. No damage to hull of boat and no indication of having struck anything..."

They shipped the broken shaft to Vancouver via P. W. A. on May 27th. and received a replacement the next day. It was immediately installed by Muir and Vic Doerksen and by seven o'clock that evening a test run had shown everything to be in order. Examination of the broken shaft had revealed a flaw in the metal, no blame could be attached to the operator, and the incident was closed.

The *Cottonwood II* suffered some rough passages around the west coast of Vancouver Island, some of which are described elsewhere. She performed her duties superbly and her skippers had nothing but praise for her. She was finally sold in 1978 to D. C. Bryan of Vancouver.

The last of the line, the *Sitka Spruce II*, worked the inside waters until she was sold in 1978.

Hank Doerksen told me, "The Blimps were a very seaworthy boat. Otherwise we couldn't have put such novices at the wheel. They were noisy, though, with that big engine immediately behind the wheelhouse. If you had somebody with you and he opened the engineroom door when you weren't expecting it, the shock of that sudden roar would be enough to send you jumping through the roof!"

He mentioned the Blimps' chief disadvantage. "They were slow boats. The engine had a recommended r. p. m. and Bob Swan at the Marine Station always used to set them well below that figure. Probably because he knew the qualifications of the people who were running them. It was a game. As soon as you left the Marine Station you monkey-wrenched the governor to get the speed up. And you made sure you knocked it down again before you took the boat back.

"It was the coming of the Union that finally killed the Blimps," said Hank sadly. "With overtime and other regulations we simply couldn't afford the slow speed any more. Now we use tupperware boats." He used the derogatory term for fibreglass hulls. "They're faster, but they're unreliable and they're not the sea boats the Blimps were..."

68

THE COASTAL STATIONS

From time to time I pulled John Paynter's leg about the arboreal monotony of the boats' names. Then one day, as I stood on the bank of the Fraser regarding two launches at the dock, fresh and sparkling from a refit, a question occurred to me.

"Why are the boats all painted grey, like dwarf battleships?"

"The fleet colour was dreamed up by somebody before my time," said John defensively.

"Yes, but why grey? Why not green, suggesting luxuriant foliage?" I warmed to my theme. "The varnished trim would represent the trunk of the mighty fir. The white cabin sides could symbolize some kind of fungoid blight. Green would be far more appropriate as a hull colour."

"Green?" He uttered a short laugh. "The staff were heartily sick of green in those days. We had a District Forester in Vancouver who was overly fond of green. He insisted that all the houses at those wretched little coastal Ranger stations be painted green. Not only that, but the staff had to paint their interior walls green, and their wood trim green, and their equipment green, and it's a wonder they didn't have to paint their families green.

"The Forest Service bought a paint by the name of Seafoam Green in vast quantities so as to get it cheaper. Then they doled it out with the rations, so to speak, and people were obligated to apply it to everything in sight. Green became an anathema."

He talked on, mentioning the flag which the launches had flown before the Maple Leaf came in: the Blue Ensign, authorized by warrant of the Governor General. But my thoughts were elsewhere, dreaming of those little green stations clinging to the fringe of the forested vastness, pounded by waves, staffed by intrepid Rangers and their little green families.

* * * * * *

In the early days a forestry station was a different thing from the present-day industrious cluster of offices and outbuildings. Frequently it consisted of one man only, operating out of his house, his principal duty being forest protection.

"The present-day industrious cluster of offices and outbuildings." Lund

Mike Halleran, collecting historical information for the Forest Service's 75th. birthday, found a set of organization charts dated 1927 to 1931 for Vancouver Forest District. Meticulously drafted on starched linen they made fascinating, if smelly, reading. Each man was indicated, together with his location and mode of transport.

A. McBride performed his duties at Sayward by means of a cycle, S. Doran at Cobble Hill had a 'Chev cat', while the luckless G. G. Menzies of Upper Pitt River used 'foot'. A. Keirstead at Owl Creek had a horse, a number of Assistant Rangers used speeders, A. W. Logan at Clo-oose favoured the canoe, while the stylish W. Waldon of Deerholme travelled by velocipede.

And S. A. Anfield, Smoke Chaser at Thurston Bay, used the *Yusella* in his headlong pursuit of wraiths. All the Vancouver boats were there, with the name of operator and site of station:

VANCOUVER FOREST DISTRICT BOAT STATIONS — 1927

Location	Officer	Boat
Harrison Hot Springs	Patrolman L.S. Wilson	Sonora
Gibson's Landing	Asst/Rgr R. W. Aylett	Check Scaler
Sechelt	Ranger I.S. Grant	Alder
Pender	Ranger R. Murray	Eunice B.
Egmont	Patrolman H. McIntosh	(private launch)
Michigan Landing	Asst/Rgr V. Brister	Madrona
Lund	Ranger E. W. Cowie	Elmera
"	Asst/Rgr S. S. Ferguson	Oak
Thurston Bay	Supervisor D. B. Taylor	Cotton-wood
" "	Ranger A. J. Mulcahy	Eva R
" "	Asst/Rgr A. C. C. Langstroth	Douglas Fir
Blind Channel	Ranger E. Hill	Kiora
Read Bay	Asst/Rgr E. J. Gregory	Cherry
Alert Bay	Ranger J. McNeill	Beatrice R
Beaver Cove	Ranger G. H. Waller	Hemlock
Quatsino	Ranger J. B. Willcock	Arbutus
Cowichan Lake	Asst/Rgr S. K. Breckenridge	Chestnut
Port Washington	Export Patrol Off. F. O'Grady	Balsam
Heriot Bay	Ranger A. H. Bromley	Oliver Clark
Whaletown	Asst/Rgr W. N. D. McKay	Sitka Spruce

* * * * * *

Time went by and the smaller stations were closed down while the big ones got bigger. Thurston Bay was the biggest, and others were built between the Thirties and the Sixties. Ganges, Chatham Channel, Echo Bay, Port Hardy, Bella Coola, Ocean Falls and others. Boats were the only means of transport between communities which are now virtually non-existent — such places as Jackson River, Apple River, Shoal Bay, East Thurlow, Echo Bay, Chatham Channel . . . . They are gone now, and the stations too.

"Many seagoing travellers coming up coast will miss one of their landmarks

"S.A. Anfield used the Yusella *in his headlong pursuit of wraiths."*

next year. As they round Root Point out of Havana Channel into Chatham Channel, they will not see the two small houses which have perched precariously on a rock bluff for these past few years. The complete Chatham Channel Ranger station is in the process of being moved . . . " So reported the News-letter in 1960.

Don Owen remarked, "Talking of privation, before we had the station at Chatham Channel there was nothing but a bloody float with a warehouse on it, and that was the Assistant Ranger's headquarters. I remember Barry Taylor spending the whole winter living there by himself, sleeping on his Blimp.

"After the station was built I remember dropping in when Jack Greenhouse was Ranger there. The office was a fourteen by twelve building at the end of the float. Then there was a walkway and a boardwalk, and two portable houses. The wives could walk from their houses to the end of the float and that was it; the rest was bush and rock rising up behind them. I remember seeing Doug Campbell's little boy in a playpen which covered the biggest flat spot of land in Chatham Channel. It was part of our responsibility to socialize when we called in, to keep the wives from going stark raving mad."

Some of the other stations were not much bigger, although the communities they served were thriving. There were herring salteries, whaling stations, canneries, and floating logging camps. These were the glory days of the Union Steamship Company. Many of the logging operations were two- to five-man shows, so the Ranger might be dealing with 50 to 60 operators in his territory.

73

Life was hard, some of the loggers returning to civilization only once a year for a big blow-out. Meanwhile, the basic needs were catered for at the logging camps, more comprehensively when a Vancouver entrepreneur conceived the notion of a floating brothel.

Hank Doerksen arrived at Thurston Bay in 1962.

"It was a dual station, East and West, with two Rangers. There were seven families on the station, with children. Years ago they'd had some real problems with the power. Electricity came from an old Pelton wheel producing direct current. New arrivals had to change all the motors on their appliances. If you put an electric kettle on you drew so much power that the whole system blew."

Wives used to teach their children with the aid of correspondence courses, and every Monday there would be a break in routine—the weekly shopping trip to Shoal Bay. Here was a little store and Post Office, originally built for the logging and fishing communities.

My idyllic imaginings of a group of people living and working together in harmony were shattered by the forthright reminiscences of one of those people:

"Little things would become very irritating. You get a bunch of people confined in a place like that and pretty soon you have a state of war. The only real break was the monthly medical trip to Campbell River, and for a time the District Forester cancelled even that."

"That sounds kind of rough," I commented.

"Everybody used to go to Campbell River in the big Ranger launch, you see, usually the *Alpine Fir*. Well, this one time the station was an armed camp and nobody would travel with anyone else. The outcome was, four ships went to Campbell River, each one containing its own little faction. But it so happened the District Forester arrived in town that day—to find the whole bloody fleet from Thurston Bay tied up there! He hit the roof. You couldn't help but see his point."

I asked Hank Doerksen about these monthly trips. He admitted the problems, but pointed out a common bond.

"Any petty irritations among the families were put aside for the purpose of presenting a united front when bargaining with stores. We got some very good deals; Overwaitea, for instance, would knock five percent off and deliver to the dock."

74   *"It wasn't uncommon to have twenty-five people on board."*

The Alpine Fir II

The voyage was quite an experience in itself. Usually the *Alpine Fir II* or the *Forest Ranger II* would be the means of transport.

"It wasn't uncommon to have twenty-five people on board. You can imagine the chaos—kids all over the place," said Hank. "I had to make a ruling that everyone stayed the hell out of the wheelhouse. Otherwise you had kids pulling throttles and shifting clutches. That's not what you want in Seymour Narrows, when you've caught the tide wrong."

Hank had an engineer on the *Alpine Fir II* who will remain nameless, but who had a firm and righteous belief in the superiority of brute strength over the crafty use of skill. On one typical Campbell River run, while Hank was threading Seymour Narrows, a wife entered the wheelhouse.

"Hank, we have a problem. The head is plugged up," she announced.

"Oh, my God," Hank groaned.

The ship was full of families. The gorilla-like engineer stood by, but he wasn't dressed for work. The chequered shirt and oily jeans had been discarded in favour of suit, white shirt and tie. He was meeting relatives from abroad

in Campbell River. Only a rat would ask a man in that finery to unplug a toilet.

"You'd better go and deal with it," Hank told him...

"So he went. And a while later I heard laughter spreading through the boat. Now, I like to run a happy ship, but I was surprised to find that this ship was happy. Then this great big bruiser appeared, and there was sewage all over him. I couldn't believe it. All over his pants and his beautiful white shirt. He was covered from head to foot in stinking, slimy sewage," said Hank, in case I hadn't got the point.

"I wanted to laugh like the others, but something in his eye told me it would be the wrong thing to do. So I told him to go forward and clean himself up as best he could. 'I'll see to the head myself,' I told him. If I'd known what I was going to find, I'd never have said that.

"There was sewage everywhere, in that head. The walls, the ceiling, the floor... All dripping with the stuff. Ugh, my God..."

It appeared that the engineer had acted without adequate planning. Instead of trying to diagnose the problem, he'd started to pump the handle. But the head was plugged solid, and all he did was to build up pressure in the system until the handle refused to budge.

He had the answer to this, however. He stood on the seat and used his foot on the handle, with a wealth of powerful thigh muscles. Pressure increased. His calves bulged like boulders. He gained another inch on the handle. In the dim recesses of his mind, he sensed triumph.

That was when the piping exploded.

So Hank cleaned up the mess and replaced the burst pipe. Step by step, carefully, he began to trace the fault back, checking the piston, the valves, the plumbing, the connections. He could find nothing wrong. The head appeared to be in perfect working order. Yet it would not perform its function.

In desperation Hank started tracing the system right through to the ocean itself. And here, at the point where Man's work was done and the blue abyss began, at the through-hull fitting there was a sea-cock.

It was shut off.

"The same bloody engineer had shut it off himself, the previous day," Hank told me ruefully, "while he was working on the plumbing. What a guy!"

But there were good times too, when any visiting boat was an excuse for a party. The staff brewed their own beer, saki, and wine; and some of the logging camps specialized in straight grain alcohol. Two old handloggers achieved fame with a product known as Loughborough Dew. When ignited, it burned with a steady flame and left no residue, and it had other properties, too. Then one day the loggers' cabin burned down, the inventory of Loughborough Dew went with it, and the coast went into mourning.

*   *   *   *   *   *

Louie Lorentsen was born in Norway and came to Canada at the age of nine. In 1933 he started part-time work on towboats, and this was the start of a long connection with the sea. He sailed on fish-packers, trollers, seiners, tankers, freighters, and even a square-rigged sailing ship brought out of retirement for service during World War II—the *Daylight*.

He told me a fascinating piece of information of no relevance to the subject of this book, but worth repeating nevertheless. A person never knows when he might need to know this:

"When you started up the diesel auxiliaries on the *Daylight* you had to have the deck hoses running. It cost us one spanker to find that out. Hot carbon would come belching out of the exhausts and set fire to the sails."

Later Louie joined the Air Force, got married, and joined the Forest Service in 1946, serving in coastal stations until 1963.

"My first station was Thurston Bay in 1946. I took the *Forest Ranger* up there from Vancouver; I was her engineer, at first. She was fifty-one foot long and built like a destroyer. Very high, somewhat unstable but quite sturdy. Then in 1948 I went to Chatham Channel when it was first opened. It was just a float with a small office building and a tool cache on it. We rented a small cabin at the head of the bay—a railroad car converted into three rooms. We lived in this until the station was built."

Louie was promoted to Ranger and given the *Western Yew*. "A beautiful boat," he said. Then in 1955 he and his wife Bunny moved to Port Hardy, started with the *Nesika* and later traded it with Echo Bay for the *Tamarack*. "We took in the whole northern end of Vancouver Island, up around Cape Scott and into Winter Harbour. The *Nesika* was seaworthy but she was very stiff. The *Tamarack* was more suitable for those waters. You could go anywhere in that boat, any time."

The story of Louie's brush with the freighter in Johnstone Straits has already been told, but he had an even more hair-raising experience with the grand old lady of the fleet, the *Beatrice R* . . .

"The grand old lady of the fleet, the Beatrice R . . . *"* In 1948.

Picture a logging operation on Browning Inlet. The crew is at lunch, sitting around the donkey-engine. From the engine a thick cable is strung across the inlet; a skyline, for hauling logs from the far shore. The cable hangs slack now, most of it underwater. A standing boom of loose logs floats at the shoreline.

The tide changes. Somebody realizes that this will cause the loose logs to drift over the submerged line, making it difficult to lift when the time comes to resume work. He fires up the donkey-engine, puts it in gear and begins to tighten the skyline. The engine note deepens after a while, and the cable ceases to wind in. From where the logger stands, he can't see the water—so he assumes logs have already drifted over the skyline.

He puts the donkey in low gear and guns it. Eventually the skyline tightens to hang, dripping, from shore to shore . . .

"We'd come into the inlet with the *Beatrice R*," said Louie. "The next thing I knew, the boat started lifting into the air. I figured we must have a tidal wave behind us. What else can you think, in good weather when a boat starts all of a sudden to roll over? The back end was lifting, and she just kept on going and going, then the wheelhouse went underwater and I was washed out of the door along with the charts, the compass and everything else that wasn't screwed down.

"I hit the water and saw the boat coming through the air, upside down, right over me. I covered my head with my hands. I thought I was going to be knocked out and drowned. I never did feel the boat hit me, though. She landed upside down, righted herself, and then I saw my assistant, Fred, thrashing with water up to his chest and shouting that he couldn't swim!"

He laughed. "But he seemed to be doing pretty good, and I figured I'd better stay the heck away from him. I had my caulk boots on, Stanfield's underwear, a heavy mac... It was winter time, and with all this wet clothing I was having a hell of a time staying afloat. Eventually I reached the standing boom and climbed up on it, saw the skyline stretched across and realized what had flipped us over. In the meantime Fred had grabbed one of the tires hanging over the side of the boat, and climbed back aboard..."

The *Beatrice R* floated near and Louie got aboard, shoved her off and let her drift up the inlet before dropping the anchor. The boat was crippled; the batteries had broken loose and smashed, and the rudder and propeller had been torn off. Eventually a Fisheries Department boat arrived and towed them into the camp.

"It wasn't until the crew came out of the woods that night that they knew what they'd done," said Louie ruefully. "We got a cup of hot coffee—much to my distress. I felt we deserved something a bit stronger than that!"

*   *   *   *   *   *

Some coastal stations were situated in larger communities. When Charlie Yingling arrived at Lund, the town had a population of fifty, which increased dramatically whenever the mail boat was due.

"There was a store, a hotel and a beer parlour," Charlie told me. "A machine shop, ways, two boat shops, a Forest Service float and an office, which was an old clam cannery on pilings over the water. I used to keep my typewriter and files on the *Dogwood*, until there got to be too much stuff."

Charlie had been on sternwheelers on the Columbia River, and his father drove the piling for the first C. P. R. bridge across that river. He joined the Forest Service at Revelstoke in 1938 and moved to Lund in 1941.

"The *Dogwood* was built by Boeings for a sports fisherman. She didn't come up to the speed they'd promised, so he refused to take delivery. He'd put a 36 h.p. Deutz diesel in her. She was a very short, stubby boat, deep in the water, with no chance of getting any speed out of her. The Deutz diesel agency used her as demonstrator for quite a while before the Forest Service bought her.

"By 1942 they'd had to replace all the planking from the waterline down. She'd been built of green fir. We used to wonder why the water poured into her. The foreman at the shop started digging into the wood, and found it was all rotten.

"At the end of the war there were no parts for the engine, so we put a GM diesel in her. We got an extra half m.p.h. out of her, but it caused her to squat. And the noise of the supercharger would drive you crazy. But she was a very safe boat in a storm."

On one occasion the *Dogwood* was involved in towing a lame *Oliver Clark* from Campbell River to Vancouver. Charlie told the story:

"We stopped at Grief Point—there was a strong south-easterly blowing— and tied up to a log boom. At eight o'clock that night the wind switched to the west and the tug started out with the boom. I jumped onto the boom and untied the lines, but when I tried to get back onto the *Dogwood* my foot slipped off the guardrail and I fell into the chuck.

"I hung onto the guyline with both hands, and for fifteen minutes I tried to get back into the boat while I was being dragged along. Art Bouch and my engineer were in the wheelhouse, and they never even looked out to see why I hadn't come back. In the end I managed to get my leg over the rail. By that time I was pretty near frozen—it was in the middle of winter. That was the narrowest squeak I ever had."

Later the *Dogwood* was involved in a famous sinking incident. After she was raised, the bows were rebuilt and the engine removed. Charlie spoke to Tommy Edwards.

"I wouldn't mind buying the old girl if she's sound."

But Tommy said, "Leave her alone, Charlie. We put her together to sell."

*   *   *   *   *   *

Varied experiences...

Lew King said, "I was at Alert Bay one winter during the war. At that time we were watching for Japanese incendiary balloons. They told us not to tell anyone if we saw any, because they didn't want Japan to know if they were getting through. We never saw any. I'm not convinced they ever existed."

Russ Campbell mentioned another aspect: "Being a Ranger in isolated places, you find yourself doing ambulance work. In the early days at Port McNeill we'd often be involved in ferrying people to the nearest hospital because the town didn't have one."

One time the *Western Yew* was involved. "A kid had been in a car accident and the mother was in hysterics. It was dark and blowing a gale—it always was, when you had to do an emergency run. I couldn't roust anybody out to go with me, but I got the mother and son into the boat all the same, and fired up. The only problem was, I'd forgotten we always leave the galley window open.

"We got out into the Straits between Port McNeill and Alert Bay, and it was really rough. The *Western Yew* was rolling like a pig. And what I didn't know, we were shipping seas green through the galley window. The woman found out, though. She came out of the aftercabin in the dark and stepped into a foot of water. She went berserk."

Russ calmed the woman down and convinced her the ship was in good hands. Anyone could forget a little thing like a window. They approached the dock at Alert Bay fast, in order to gain control, and Russ laid a spring line along the deck in readiness. Nothing could have been more seamanlike than the way he slipped the gear into reverse at the exact moment, stood the *Western Yew* on her nose, pushed her into neutral and jumped to the dock.

Unfortunately the boat had a somewhat imprecise hydraulic clutch. Returning itself to forward gear, the *Western Yew* took off into the stormy night, bearing its wailing human cargo with it.

A lesser man than Russ would have taken off too, in the opposite direction, later mailing in his resignation from Lima, Peru. But Russ was a Forest Officer of the old school. He made a catlike leap at the stern of the boat as it disappeared into the blackness, clawed himself aboard, restored control and came in to the dock for a second try, exuding calmness and competence. His passenger, however, was not impressed . . .

Probably the worst effects of the remote stations were felt by the women, particularly those with children. They would suffer the problems of unreliable electricity, sewage back-ups, lack of shops, schools or hospitals, loneliness, boredom.

"The real heroes of Thurston Bay were the wives," Hank Doerksen said.

And Cecelia Sweet, wife of Jim Sweet, the deck hand of *Syrene*, gave me her views.

"When I first went to Thurston Bay I took just two bags of groceries with me. Jim hadn't told me there wasn't a store. As we came down in the float plane I saw this tiny bunch of houses and I said, 'This is it?' Well, this was Thurston Bay all right, and I'd missed the monthly shopping trip. I was in the middle of nowhere without a can opener, and the furniture wouldn't be arriving for two or three days.

"There was dust everywhere in that house. And there were mice. As you lay in bed at night you could hear them pittering above in the ceiling, and when you got up in the morning there'd be little turds all over the place. One evening I rebelled. I said to Jim, 'I refuse to go to bed until you find that mouse I can hear in there.' And Jim searched, but the mouse had scuttled down a crack."

But they were adaptable, those women.

"Jim fibreglassed the bottom of his little dinghy on a warm day, but it turned cold so the fibreglass wouldn't set. He carted the boat into the living room. It sat there for weeks on end. I remember Maureen Maxwell came in one time and said, 'Jeez, I love your coffee table.'"

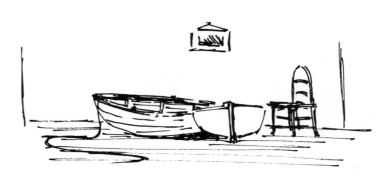

Back in 1914 a boat took shape on the west coast of Vancouver Island. Almost nothing is known of her now; neither her length nor her beam, nor even her general appearance. One thing is known: that she was around for thirty years, although by the end of that period we can suppose that she was not in the best condition—or they wouldn't have done what they did to the old *Bonila Rock*.

In 1944 another war was in progress, and a Tofino man wanted a new boat. The authorities wouldn't let him build it, wartime restrictions being what they were. Maintenance only was the rule. Casting around for a solution to this problem, the man came up with a bright idea. He would take the old *Bonila Rock* and have her rebuilt like new.

So they hauled the old boat up onto the ways and began to strip her down, and by the time they'd removed the rotten timbers there wasn't a hell of a lot left; just the keel and a few ribs. But she was still legally the old *Bonila Rock*, in the process of being rebuilt.

In due course the Federal Inspector made the arduous trip to Tofino, saw the work in progress, gave his approval and hurried back to civilization. He'd hardly disappeared over the horizon before they'd sawn up the keel and ribs and pushed them out of the door, and started again with a new keel.

In due course a fine new boat emerged from the yards, fifty-three feet overall with a fifteen foot beam. Her name was the *Bonila Rock*, in deference to officialdom. Two pieces from the old *Bonila Rock* remained: the tow bitt and a manhole on the afterdeck. The tow bitt was useless; it was mounted too far astern, and so hindered the boat from turning when she was towing. The manhole may well have been quite useful.

In 1948 the Forest Service became aware that activity on the west coast of Vancouver Island was on the upsurge, "so much so that we are confident it will be necessary before long to have a Ranger stationed permanently on the west coast." That same memorandum said, "We have canvassed the situation here around the Vancouver waterfront and have found a launch which we think would be very suitable for our requirements... This launch is in very good shape... Her construction is bordering on the massive... The boat in question is named the *Bonila Rock*."

*   *   *   *   *   *

"She was a well-built boat."

John Paynter and I drove out to Lantzville one day to visit Frank Tannock, who had spent most of his working life in the Forest Service and was now retired in a medium-sized house and surrounded by memorabilia. He was very ready to talk about the old days.

"The first boat I was on was the *Yellow Cedar*. I took her out when we first bought her—she was named the *Bonila Rock*, then. I picked her up at the marine depot and called in at Victoria, where we almost had a fire on board. Smoke was everywhere. We pulled the panels off and found the exhaust pipe hadn't been lagged with asbestos...

"When I was Ranger on the west coast everything went very well. Bailey was my captain on the *Yellow Cedar*. She was a well-built boat. She had to be, to take the punishment of that coast."

And Bailey was an excellent captain, by all accounts. An outspoken Australian, he was once involved in a classic verbal exchange with Art Bouch, the dapper boss of the *Syrene*.

The Captain's usual adversary was the Ranger, however. In the early days the responsibilities of the Captain vis-a-vis the Ranger had not been clearly defined. Launch Captains felt that they were in charge of their vessel and everything connected with the running of it. Rangers felt that they were answerable to Headquarters for everything that happened in their bailiwick, and that included the launch. Headquarters pussyfooted around the issue.

"We only have Captains on the big crew-carrying boats as a general rule,"

John Paynter informed me. "The *Yellow Cedar* was unique among Vancouver District Ranger launches in having a skipper. The circumstances of that coast-line demanded it."

In 1952 the situation flared up. By that time Captain J. Evelyn was in charge of the *Yellow Cedar* and the Ranger of the time had questioned his competency—although reading between the lines, personality problems had been aggravated by lack of Headquarters direction. "Captain Evelyn would like a written definition of the extent of his responsibility and authority," the investigators wrote.

It was bad luck for Captain Evelyn that, just over one month later, he put the *Yellow Cedar* on an uncharted rock. ". . . He is known to be a very efficient and careful navigator," said the District Forester in his report. "In view of his past performance and the knowledge that such an accident could occur to any man navigating on the west coast, we are inclined to deal with this accident in a lenient manner . . ."

Now we go forward in time to the late Fifties. Ranger, cook, skipper and supervisor Frank Tannock are on board.

The accident report stated baldly:

"At approximately 0845 hours Capt ———— was advised to proceed to Tofino with a call at Hot Springs Cove. It was noted fog was clearing to the S. W.

"Ranger went below to work on reports.

"At 0940 hours *Yellow Cedar* hit something and came to a very abrupt stop. I would say we were travelling at full speed when we hit object. Sup. Tannock and cook were in the wheelhouse at the time."

It had all the trappings of high drama, and Sup. Tannock, now retd., was sitting there before us, affable and willing to talk.

"What happened, Frank?" I asked.

He chuckled. "I'd been out to Tahsis to meet Larry Ormond, the Ranger there. We were heading from Gold River to Nootka, going between Verdia and Bligh Islands in Nootka Sound. I'd said to Larry, 'What's he going through this passage for?' My recollection was that Captain Bailey never used to go through there, because there wasn't enough information on the charts. 'I think he's just trying to show off because you're on board,' said Larry.

"He'd hardly got the words out of his mouth when—whump! Whump! Whump! And we were hard aground on the rocks. I stepped into the wheelhouse and said to the skipper, 'Did you draw a course through here?'

'Oh, yes,' he said. He showed me the chart, and sure enough there was a course pencilled through.

"But then I spotted something. I took an eraser and rubbed part of the line out—and there were little dots on the chart there. He'd drawn his course straight over the rocks!" Frank laughed heartily. "But he was right on course. There was no argument about that!"

Harry Hill was in charge of the Marine Station at the time, and he and Tommy Edwards flew out in an old Junkers to inspect the damage. Tommy took up the story:

"We had no cement so we got canvas groundsheets, tied ropes on them and pulled them over the outside of the bow. Then we steamed for Tahsis. They did a darned good job at the yard there. The rock had taken a right-angled bite out of the forefoot, and they made a new forefoot out of a tree around there. It's probably still in her."

*   *   *   *   *   *

Some years ago I spent an idyllic few days on the *Yellow Cedar*. We cruised around the waters north of Tofino, past Vargas and Flores Islands, visiting logging camps along the way and finishing up at Hot Springs Cove. Here we walked the enchanting boardwalk through the rain forest to the hot pools, took off our clothes and bathed in the cool April sunlight. I will always remember those few days; the rocky bluffs looming from the calm waters, the forests and the little outposts of humanity, the deck of the *Yellow Cedar* drumming softly beneath my feet, the bubbling wake ruler-straight. Evenings at anchor, easy conversation in the cabin, a game of crib and a nightcap; then to bed, rocked to sleep by the gentle motion of the boat.

The captain of the *Yellow Cedar* in those days was Bordie Grant. Medium height with a smiling face, he took his duties very seriously but was always ready to relax and join in the general conversation and light-hearted banter once those duties were over. I took a photograph of him staring intently into the fog as we swept out of Tofino, watching for deadheads, shoals, buoys, other craft and the myriad hazards of the coast.

Bordie retired in 1974 and the *Yellow Cedar* left Tofino soon afterwards, when it was decided that her work could more effectively be handled by smaller, faster boats stationed at several bases on the coast. Later I heard that Bordie was sick, and that the prognosis was not good. Small, sad bits of news

"Visiting logging camps along the way.."

came through the grapevine: Bordie had lost the use of his legs, he was in a wheelchair, his hands were going.

John Paynter and I went to visit him. He lived in a neat little bungalow in Tofino, and both he and his wife were pleased to see us. I was concerned that we might overtire him, sitting there firing questions at him with a tape recorder going; but he said he would be fine. We'd warned him we were coming and he'd been looking forward to it—although he didn't think he'd have much of interest to tell us, because everything had gone very smoothly during his eighteen years as captain of the *Yellow Cedar*. But he'd be very happy to talk, all the same. He was much thinner than I remembered him, but his voice was strong as we talked about the boat he loved.

"She's only fifty-two feet long, and you know what the winters are like off the west coast. It's always rough. You get off Estevan in a storm and you have to make a decision: do you try to get around or do you turn back? If you don't get around now, you might be tied up for a week away from base waiting for the weather. But off Estevan it might be just about as much as the boat can take. Lots of times we took a beating. But that's one thing I liked about the west coast—it was a challenge. When we did get back to port after a harrowing trip, it was always such a relief and gave you such a sense of accomplishment. In the early days, all we had was a compass to navigate by. In wintertime we'd get heavy blows and rain and you couldn't see a thing. There'd be fog. You'd be running up the coast without radar or an echo sounder, going by dead reckoning, and you didn't know what your drift was..."

There was no rancour in his voice as he voiced every field man's complaint: the lack of understanding at Headquarters.

"They weren't sea minded. They thought in terms of the Fraser River and the Gulf of Georgia. The *Yellow Cedar* was the only vessel on the west coast without radar. When they finally gave me radar, they admitted they were unhappy about it. They said it was the thin end of the wedge."

Navigation was not the only problem.

"She had no bilge pump off the main engine. I said to the engineer at the Marine Station, 'Give us a pump, for goodness sake. There's nothing but a hand pump down in the engine room. If anything goes seriously wrong, nobody can pump for long down there.' And do you know what he said? He said, 'Then you just run her up on a beach.' I told him, 'We're not talking about the Fraser River. We try to stay off the beaches on the west coast!'" Where the rollers come all the way from Japan...

They gave Bordie his pump, but only after he'd nearly lost the *Yellow Cedar* in dirty weather off Estevan. She was pounding heavily and, worried about a plank springing, Bordie went below to take a look around. He found his stateroom full of water, and the engineroom floor had begun to flood. A circulation pipe had broken. The engineer did the best he could, swathing the pipe in rags. The Ranger used the hand pump, but the heat in the engine room was so intense that he could only work a couple of minutes at a time. Meanwhile Bordie stood at the wheel and the engineer struggled with the leak.

When finally they made Nootka, Bordie had much to say about the situation. The Ranger, exhausted, had to agree. They could have lost the ship and their lives too, just for the lack of a proper bilge pump. He contacted Headquarters and the pump was installed.

In the early days Bordie experienced the usual conflicts of authority.

"Rangers would come from the east coast of the Island, where they'd been in charge of their launch. Out here, they found they had a skipper with a ticket — but they still didn't want to give up their authority. We'd argue. 'Am I supposed to be just a passenger on this boat?' they'd ask. I'd tell them, 'Look on it as your private yacht. You can tell me where you want to go, but how it's done is up to me!'

"When I joined the Forest Service, the Ranger office was on the boat. Around 1959 they started to build the Ranger station — Larry Ormond was all by himself there. He used to call himself the Lone Ranger. They wanted me to do odd jobs around the station when the boat wasn't in use. I told them — 'I've dug ditches before and I'll probably dig them again, but right now I'm the captain of the *Yellow Cedar* and I'm not digging ditches!'"

He laughed. "I had one Ranger who figured he could take charge. 'I've been four years deep sea,' he told me. He made the first trip with us and, well, it was dirty weather. Blowing. Rough. And I don't suppose he'd ever been off the west coast in a little boat before. Well, he spent his time in his bunk all the way to Nootka. Sick! He was man enough to come to me when the trip was over and say, 'Bordie, this is real deep sea stuff and it's your job. I don't want any part of it.'"

Bordie was born in Silverton and came to Tofino when he was three years old, at which time only half a dozen families lived there. His father worked at a local mine, and when it closed down times became hard. But the years went by and things got better, and after Bordie left school they bought a thirty foot launch and built up a passenger and mail trade. There was no road, so Bordie would pick up visitors at Grice Bay and ferry them to Tofino for $5 a head.

In 1942 he volunteered for the Navy but was turned down for health reasons. He went herring fishing, married a Tofino girl, and although by now he had plenty of practical experience and job offers, he didn't want to leave Tofino. So, finally, he joined the *Yellow Cedar*.

"In the old days you had to fit your life into the needs of the job. When we went up the coast for a couple of weeks the Ranger would have a certain amount of work he'd want to get done. We didn't care what hours we put in. The idea was to get the work done, then get home." He sighed. "In the later days it changed. You put the hours in, then you headed back with the job half finished. I couldn't get used to that."

At first the *Yellow Cedar* was used only during the summer, but as logging activity increased the work became year-round and a Blimp was stationed at

Tofino as an assistant Ranger boat for the summer months. The *Yellow Cedar* would escort them from Vancouver in the spring, and back in the fall.

"They were fine little boats, the Blimps," Bordie said, "but it was really too much for them in the fall. We'd get into some bad blows; although it was surprising what those little boats could take. I remember I was escorting the *Douglas Fir II* south one fall; she'd been in Nootka Sound all summer. It started to blow south-east. I thought to myself, 'Gee, I think we can make it. But if we don't make it today, it'll be quite a few days before we can get her around.'

"So I kept going with the *Yellow Cedar*, kind of sucking the *Douglas Fir II* along behind. But she kept dropping back, dragging a little further behind, until all I could see was a bank of foam back there. At last the Ranger called me on the radio. 'Look,' he said, 'we can't take any more.' So we turned around and went back. That was one we lost, but we won a few, too." He was silent for a moment, remembering.

He spoke of other boats: the *Nesika*, the *Conifer II* at Alberni. The time he and another captain brought the *Island Scaler* round. Then talk returned to the Blimps and the escort duties.

"Another time Ted McArthur was on the *Cottonwood II*. We hit bad north-easters all the way south. And around Victoria way, across Race Rocks to Trial Island, all I could see behind me was foam, and somewhere in there was the *Cottonwood II*. But we kept her coming. We got into the Marine Station, and when I went down to pick up the boats some time later one of the fellows said to me, 'What did you do to the *Cottonwood II*? She's awash with water right up under the bunks, and everywhere is soaking!' Well, it was from that trip. It came in through the ventilators, around the doors—it was squirting in through every little crack.

"No, nothing much happened during those eighteen years," he said; and I suppose to a real seaman nothing did. He sailed the west coast with caution and skill and he came through it without a serious accident. So naturally he would think nothing had happened. But as we talked, I saw towering seas and the *Yellow Cedar* plunging like a whale, hungry rocks to her lee, waiting, always there. Eighteen years of that.

"Seventy-five percent of seamanship is staying out of trouble," he said. "Twenty-five percent is after you've got into it." And for once his quiet modesty disappeared, and he spoke with pride and conviction. "I was great at sensing the weather. Being a fisherman I had a feel for it. Often I'd turn back because I knew it'd be worse further on. The next day I might go out in rougher weather, but I'd know it would get better. The Rangers wouldn't always understand that. Often I'd be thinking of conditions at our destination, too. Take a place like Esperanza. In winter you might get big seas there when the tide's ebbing. If the breakers catch you, you could get smashed up. So if we were running a little late for the tide, I'd turn back. I'd stay out of trouble . . . "

And so the old captain talked on, telling us stories of the wild west coast. Another story of *Cottonwood II* and a storm that hit off Estevan, just after dawn. A run for shelter, and six days stormbound. A time in Kyoquot, stormbound for nine days that time, playing crib all hours of the day and night with Hank Doerksen. More tales of his sixth sense for the weather. The times he'd roused the crew in the middle of the night because he'd awakened and something had told him: '*Bordie, you've got to get going . . .*'

Finally we left him there, sitting in his wheelchair; a sick man, but a man fulfilled. "If I'd had to do all those eighteen years over again," he said at the end, "I don't see how I could have improved on my handling of the boat."

I wish I could be so sure of my own competence.

"We've got some good stuff there, Mike," said John as we drove away.

"I hope I can do it justice," I said.

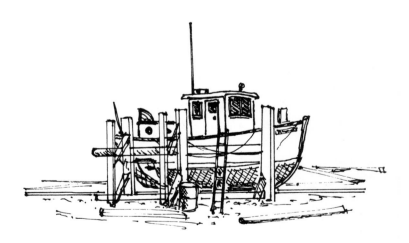

SCALING

"In the old days we'd live in a camp. They treated us royally, the loggers did. You see, things were different in those days. Our scale—our measurement of the wood, that is—wasn't only used for collection of stumpage by the Government. It was an important measure for barter between buyer and seller. Nowadays, the scaler is looked on as just another tax collector." He grinned ruefully. "You can imagine what that means. But in the old days, the scaler was the kingpin of the woods."

I'd driven through the drizzling November rain in search of Larry Coles. 'Turn right at the church, then the first house on the right—you'll see the name COLES on a tree.'

Larry had taken me into the living room and we'd sat on a chesterfield beside the window. The house was hidden from the world by a tall, dense cedar hedge, planted many years ago. "Forest Service stock," he told me, as though it was a guarantee of quality. There were photographs of mountains on the walls and a flattering representation of the Marine Building, where the Forest Service had its Vancouver office. There were no pictures of England; nothing except Larry's accent to tell me he came from the Old Country.

"Born in Tooting, near London," he told me. "My wife's from Scotland." He looked like a Londoner too, a small, wiry man, thin-faced with a quick smile.

And so we talked of bygone days. Based at the Marine Building, Larry would spend a month at a time up the coast: Knight Inlet, Seymour Inlet, Minstrel Island—all the scattered, isolated logging camps of that wild and remote area.

"I'd be away for thirty days," he said, "and I'd sleep in twenty-nine different beds on the circuit."

"How did you get there from Vancouver?"

"Union Steamship. And sometimes we flew in the old Stranraers of Queen Charlotte Airlines. When we arrived, we depended on the logger to take us from camp to camp as the need for a scaler arose. We didn't have a boat up there, not then."

"But there were scaling boats in those days, weren't there? I know they bought a boat called *Gwen* way back in 1914."

"Yes." He thought for a moment. "Before we started to work out of the

94

"They bought a boat called Gwen *way back in* 1914.*"*

Marine Building, there was one boat in Coal Harbour. She was called the *Scaler*, built in 1924." A long time afterwards I came across an ancient photograph of the *Scaler*, showing her to be a boxy fifty footer with a distinctly top-heavy look. A wheelhouse sat centrally atop long fore and aft cabins, affording plenty of accommodation. "There were quite a number of sawmills on the North Shore, and the holding grounds were over at Moodyville, between the First and Second Narrows bridge. The boat took the scalers to those booms."

I hesitated. "What did the scalers do, exactly?"

He looked at me. "You don't know what scaling is, do you? Not many people do. Sometimes they think it has to do with fish."

"I know it has to do with logs. I don't know exactly how it's done, that's all."

His voice changed, and I knew he was repeating something he'd said many times before, in front of many audiences. "Scaling," he said, "is the measurement and quantification of all forest products. That includes Christmas trees, telephone poles, shakes, pitprops and all minor products."

"I came across an ancient photograph of the Scaler.*"*

"Yes, but how is it *done?*"

"Well, the logger calls the scaling dispatcher first, to tell him there's a boom of logs needs scaling. The dispatchers send the scalers to the booms—although sometimes it's not so simple as that. Sometimes the scaler can't find the boom. You'd think a big thing like a boom of logs couldn't get lost; but it happens. Sometimes the towboat didn't tell the logger the boom was moved. All kinds of things. It all wastes the time of the scaler."

"What does the scaler do when he finds the boom? Eventually, I mean."

"Nowadays he measures the top and butt diameters, and the length. He calculates the volume from this. Then he takes into account the quality—whether the wood is rotten or split, or whatever. This volume forms the basis of the stumpage the logger pays to the Crown. So you can see how important the scaler's job is."

But I was more interested in the raw mechanics. "He crawls over the floating logs and measures them with a stick?"

"That's it. Although we're getting more into dry-land sorts these days. And inland we use weight-scaling, of course."

I was still visualizing the stick-wielding scaler, leaping from log to log, goat-like. "I expect they sometimes fall in."

96

"They wear life-jackets." Larry's face clouded. "A stupid regulation, if you ask me."

"How's that?"

"Well, you think of a man falling off a log boom when there's a current running. The water takes him under the boom. Can he swim out from there? No, he can't. The life-jacket's holding him up against the underside of the logs. So he drowns."

We pondered the uncertainties of life for a moment while Larry brought out the Ne Plus Ultra scotch and the rain pattered against the window.

Much later I came across a reference to the *Scaler* in an old ledger giving carefully handwritten details of some of the boats in service shortly after World War II; and then I found an old file index which mentioned that *Scaler* had been renamed *Gleam* on sale. Nothing else. No dimensions or dates; just a note that the file had been destroyed, years ago.

And looking through the old Annual Reports I found that the *Scaler* was bought in 1925 for the then-princely sum of $6500. Oddly enough, a launch named *Gleam* had been bought in 1919 for $1948.66. The fate of *Gleam* can only be guessed at but her name, it seems, was resurrected.

"We got rid of the *Scaler* round about the time Lion's Gate Bridge was built," he said. "The bridge made transportation easier. We located the new boat at Fisherman's Cove. The scalers would go to the Cove by car, then by boat to Andy's Bay, Long Bay, Centre Bay; and return daily."

"What was the name of the new boat?"

"The *A. L. Bryant*," he said . . .

"Wasn't that the boat that sank?"

So he told me.

*   *   *   *   *   *

The afternoon of October 3rd., 1950 was calm, the sea still. The sky was overcast and a light haze drifted across the waters from the direction of Vancouver Island, where slash-burning was in progress, lending the air a faint tang of wood smoke. Visibility was good as the *A. L. Bryant* ploughed southward down Howe Sound. Some distance behind her the Union Steamship *Lady Cynthia* could be seen, following a similar course. Otherwise there was little traffic.

The *A. L. Bryant* was a solid, upright craft of no-nonsense appearance, forty-two feet long with a beam of nine feet six inches, propelled by a Hall Scott 100 h. p. engine. Bought in 1928 from the Marine Transit Co. she'd had, in recent years, a series of mishaps. In June of 1950 she'd been rammed by a tug in Centre Bay, Gambier Island; and in September she'd had a brush with a powerboat in Fisherman's Cove. And back on October 4th, 1930 — twenty years ago — she'd been mauled by the West Vancouver ferry *Sonrisa* as she backed from the dock.

Named after a legendary Scaling Superintendent in the days before John Paynter began to comb the forests for boat names, the *A. L. Bryant* had a simple, practical layout. The wheelhouse rose from a short, high foredeck; aft of this and under a coach roof some three feet lower came the engine room and, further aft, the cabin for scalers. The roof was cluttered with an assortment of vents and hatchways, plus a small funnel and a dinghy.

All this tended to restrict visibility from the wheelhouse aft, which may or may not have had some bearing on what happened on that fateful afternoon.

At four o'clock the *A. L. Bryant* was rounding Hood Point on Bowen Island. She was captained by J. W. McDonald, with J. H. Kilby keeping him

company in the wheelhouse. In the cabin sat five scalers on their way home, working on their tally sheets by the light from the six large, square windows. There was little conversation. Along the starboard side sat F. A. Longstaff and W. M. Ingram, and on the port side were Frank Patterson, Larry Coles and finally Pete Wrotnowski, who had lost an arm in Italy and had been used by the Government as an example of how a man could rehabilitate himself by re-learning manual skills with his remaining hand.

Five men going home, sitting in the warm cabin, checking off their papers, lulled by the drumming of the engine immediately forward of the cabin—and, because of that, unable to hear the roar of nemesis bearing down on them.

Then the glistening black bow of the *Lady Cynthia* sliced into the cabin with a huge splintering of timbers.

The *A. L. Bryant* jerked and rolled, the way a whale does when a harpoon explodes in her guts.

The scalers had little time to react. Longstaff plunged for the engine room, the wall of *Lady Cynthia's* hull passing inches behind him. Wrotnowski made for the hatch, flinging himself at the short companionway and beginning to climb, handicapped by his lost arm. Larry Coles grabbed the rail to follow. Then the cabin rolled again, and the cold waters closed over the men, and the dark underbelly of the *Lady Cynthia* surged past them.

The *A. L. Bryant* was mortally wounded. The *Lady Cynthia* had cut her cleanly in half just aft of the engine room. The forward end floated away, the twisted propeller shaft carving a wide and useless arc through the black water. McDonald climbed out of the wheelhouse onto the canted foredeck. Kilby was there too.

The after end of the *A. L. Bryant* rolled past the flank of the *Lady Cynthia*, under the wide platform which ran just above the ship's waterline.

Coles, Wrotnowski and Ingram broke surface near the stern of the *Lady Cynthia*. Patterson and Longstaff were nowhere to be seen. The after end of the *A. L. Bryant* drifted near. Larry Coles caught hold of the stern rail. With the other hand he grabbed the one-armed Wrotnowski's shoulder harness. Wrotnowski still held his cigarette holder clamped between his teeth. He spat it out to suck air, and gasped, "My God!" These were the first words anyone had spoken since the *Lady Cynthia's* bows had burst into the cabin. Ingram was struggling nearby. Wrotnowski caught hold of him and Coles began to pull them both to safety.

Then the *Lady Cynthia* reversed screws.

"A solid, upright craft of no-nonsense appearance."

Coles heard the thunder of cavitation, saw the bubbling as the huge propellers began to bite into the water, felt the ocean tremble as the towering bulk of the ship dragged itself to a halt. Wrotnowski was plucked from his grasp and both he and Ingram were sucked into the deadly churning. Coles felt the stern of the *A. L. Bryant* swing towards the propellers as he pulled himself on board, his legs inches from the whirling blades.

Lying there on the bobbing afterdeck, trembling with fear and cold, Coles realized for the first time that the entire forward end of the boat was missing. The wrecked stern would not stay afloat for long. But above him loomed the *Lady Cynthia*, and people were throwing lifebelts and ropes down. Wrotnowski and Ingram had disappeared. Coles did not want to look at the water. Instead he looked up at the Union Steamship, and when the main heaving line came snaking down from above he caught hold of it and threw it around his waist, knotting it tightly.

"Pull!" he shouted.

And then occurred one of those moments of black comedy which are funny only in retrospect. The crew of the *Lady Cynthia* hauled away. The rope tightened around Coles' midriff, but his feet refused to leave the deck. The crew pulled harder, the passengers shouting encouragement. Coles' face became empurpled as the rope gripped his waist like a tourniquet, but he remained obstinately aboard the remains of the *A. L. Bryant* as though bound there by invisible bonds of loyalty.

In fact, as he soon realized, he was bound there by the rope. In throwing it around his waist he had encircled the flagstaff which was welded to the stern rail. Understanding his frantic signals the crew slackened off, Coles freed himself and retied the rope, and the rescue operation recommenced. Now, in the haste of the moment — McDonald and Kilby were drifting away on the water-logged bow, and the injured Patterson could be heard shouting from the water — a further mistake was made. Instead of being untied at the cargo deck, Coles was hauled all the way to the main deck, swinging against the hull and suffering injuries to head and shoulder.

It is unfair to judge mistakes made in moments of crisis. When McDonald and Kilby were finally rescued from the floating bows, nobody thought to look in the flooded engine room. It is just possible that Longstaff was still alive in there. The bow section of the *A. L. Bryant* drifted near Gibsons the following day and his body was found jammed against the engine. The final chapter of the tragedy was related by Tommy Edwards.

"Bob Swan took the *B. C. Forester* and some of the boys, and they got two logs and tied them alongside the wreck. They floated her ashore, took out the engine and burned her. But the after half—we never did know what happened to it. The end of the shaft . . . I'll never forget that. It looked just as though you'd wrung it off."

The bodies of Wrotnowski and Ingram were never found.

*   *   *   *   *   *

"They took Frank Patterson straight to hospital," said Larry. "It was only because of his mental and physical strength that he lived. As it was, he lost an arm."

"How about you?" I asked. It was still raining outside; fitting weather for this sad tale. The tall trees moved and shed leaves in the November wind.

"I remember . . . My wife was expecting a baby. They took me from the dock wrapped in a Union Steamship blanket—no shoes, no clothes—and rushed me to our little wartime home in North Van. Later I got into quite a hectic discussion with the District Forester of the time, who claimed I'd publicized the event. I had difficulty in assuring him," he looked at me without a hint of a smile, "that my wife and I being of British descent we just don't publicize things like that. You could see that in the following day's paper—everybody's picture was in there except yours truly . . . "

There was a formal investigation, of course. Most of the evidence on the first day concerned the steering apparatus on the *Lady Cynthia*. It seemed the vessel had a 'slow wheel'—in fact, the helmsman stated that he was unable to turn the wheel more than half a revolution to port, after which it stuck fast. Mr. Strang, the *Lady Cynthia's* Chief Officer, had then seized the wheel, jerked it clear and put it hard aport.

The scene was re-enacted in the courtroom, and in a tense silence the slim, serious-faced officer hauled at a stubborn, imaginary wheel. Finally: "Hard aport, sir," he said; and the stopwatch was consulted. It had taken twenty seconds . . .

But testimony conflicted, and some claimed that the *A. L. Bryant* had swung off course, across the path of the *Cynthia*. Mr. Bird, representing the Union Steamship Company, submitted that the *Bryant's* captain did not maintain an adequate lookout aft, knowing that he would soon be overtaken. And in the end the blame was attached equally to the two ships.

"I couldn't agree with that," said Larry darkly. "I'd seen the *Lady Cynthia* following us down Howe Sound earlier. She was the overtaking vessel and the rules of the road state that the overtaking vessel must give way. And anyway," he echoed the words of Louie Lorentsen, "how could the captain of the *Bryant* keep a lookout aft when he's watching the water ahead for deadheads and such? It was a miscarriage of justice."

"Poor old Wardy McDonald never got over it," Don Owen told me. "Whenever we'd have a few drinks, by about the second drink he'd be reliving it. It became an obsession with him, that he was responsible for the death of those guys. He sure got a bum deal in the investigation."

Possibly. Who knows, now? Perhaps a passenger on the *Lady Cynthia* still retains in his mind's eye a true image of those fateful few seconds, when the *A. L. Bryant* died and took three men with her. But such images fade like old photographs until the only thing we are left with is the knowledge that three men died thirty years ago, and it need not have happened.

*　　*　　*　　*　　*　　*

For a short time after the accident they rented boats to take the scalers to their work and then, in 1951, a large and stylish craft was bought. Over sixty feet long with a sleek, wooden semi-planing hull and twin Jimmies she had originally been built in 1944 as a U. S. N. rescue launch. Now she bore the name of *Flying Saucer*—a title with connotations of such mystery and headlong speed that it proved altogether too rich for the Forest Service's blood. So they renamed her *B. C. Scaler*.

They built a new wheelhouse above the existing deckhouse, enlarged the trunk cabin and added a short funnel. The bullet-proof, self-sealing gas tanks were replaced and she was repainted in the company colours. Like the *A. L. Bryant*, she was berthed at Fisherman's Cove, and it seems that it took a little while for this skittish filly to realize that she had become a workhorse.

"We had dozens of complaints at the booming grounds," said Larry. It seemed that the ex-*Flying Saucer* threw up quite a wash as she hurtled into the smaller bays. "But we got twenty-six years of service out of her. Very little trouble; just the occasional bent shaft or propeller when we'd run into a deadhead."

In the end she became a victim of the shorter work week. Operating out of Fisherman's Cove, it became impossible to do an honest day's work at the

*"The ex-*Flying Saucer *threw up quite a wash."*

extreme points of the Howe Sound booming grounds, so a group of resident scalers was built up in the Gibsons area and the *B. C. Soaler* felt the chill wind of redundancy. In 1977 she was sold to West Coast Salvage of Vancouver. The *Island Scaler* was transferred to Gibsons and she is there still, assisted by a twenty-four foot fibreglass landing craft known simply as *L C* 17.

*   *   *   *   *   *

Previously the *Island Scaler* had been stationed at Port Alberni. She was a new departure for the Forest Service, being a thirty-four foot houseyacht design, bought in 1971. This configuration appealed to John Paynter because of the beaminess. Scalers are bulky people. Heavily clad for outdoor work, carrying lunch packs, tally boards and scaling sticks, they take up a lot of room on a boat. Any apprehensions John may have felt in buying a pleasure boat for this purpose were dispelled when he discovered that the same firm had just fitted out a similar vessel as a marine school bus for taking children across Prince Rupert harbour.

There was a voyage around the west coast of Vancouver Island to be faced, however. It was a long, rough trip for an untried boat.

"So we put two captains on board," John told me.

I was sure there was logic in this but it escaped me for the moment, and John seemed to consider his explanation sufficient. So I allowed a decent silence to fall before I queried the situation.

"One of the captains had a history of heart trouble," John elaborated. "But they both reported that the boat handled beautifully."

She had twin screws, another curious anomaly. One of the problems in operating launches in booming grounds is the lurking presence of dead-heads—the unseen logs floating end up, which play havoc with propellers. Through some strange perverseness of fate, however, it seems that the scaling service kept finding itself with twin-screwed boats, where the chances of damage are doubled. However, in five years service at Port Alberni the *Island Scaler* had an uneventful history.

*   *   *   *   *   *

In the mid-coast area lay the booming grounds of Ocean Falls, and history here begins in 1924. The Annual Report for that year records the purchase of a scaling vessel named *Swifter*. A swifter, Larry Coles informs me, is the top log on a boom, placed at right angles to the direction of the others.

Swifter served Ocean Falls without recorded incident until she was replaced in 1940 by *Swifter II*, a neat twenty-six footer built by Armstrong Brothers of Victoria especially for the job. Powered by a sixty horsepower Kermath engine, she lasted nine years. It had become increasingly apparent that small runabouts would handle the work more efficiently, and she was sold in 1949.

Scaling boats had appeared rather mysteriously in Prince Rupert. In the early Fifties the scaling staff there, casting off the Headquarters yoke, had independently bought four little fibreglass boats from North West Plastic in Vancouver, and named them.

"They were called the *Essenar I to IV*," John said, "and they gave good service for many years. Scaling service is hard on a boat, you know—chafing alongside log booms and boom chain toggles."

I had a feeling that the origin of the curious name *Essenar* was fated to remain a mystery, like *Embree*, but John offered a flash of enlightenment.

"It eluded me for a long time, too. Then I realized it was a phonetic representation of S & R, Stumpage and Royalty. I didn't perpetuate the name, and when the *Essenars* were finally disposed of we moved the *Juniper III* up there—she was a Falconer Marine twenty-six footer with a Chrysler engine. She wasn't the ideal boat and in 1969 we bought the *Northern Scaler* and sent her up there."

The *Northern Scaler* was a failure or, as John put it, 'not an unqualified success.' Years later, I can recall seeing her myself, lying idle at Van Isle Marina in Sidney, awaiting the occasional use of the Langford Ranger. She had the useless, dispirited look of a deposed Latin American President in exile.

She was a twenty-eight foot fibreglass cabin cruiser based on a stock model, with a 6V-53 GM diesel with a vee-drive and a boarding platform at the stern. The drive incorporated a sophisticated coupling, made by a space-age company, which duly self-destructed shortly after launching while the boat was doing some twelve knots.

The momentum of the boat caused the propeller to keep going, flogging the amputated stub shaft around the bottom of the boat like a flail. The boat remained afloat, convincing the operator of the durability of fibreglass. This only partly compensated for his loss of confidence in space-age couplings.

She quickly became an unpopular boat. She was noisy and she had a vibration problem, and she was difficult to get into and out of, at log booms. She remained ill-starred to the bitter end.

In 1976 she lay disgraced alongside a merchant ship in Prince Rupert harbour, waiting to be loaded aboard before her final trip into exile, when a sudden storm sprang up from the west. While the crew were eating lunch, the waves began to break against her stern and, aided by the boarding platform, to flood the cockpit.

"*Swifter II, a neat twenty-six footer.*"

The crew returned. Somebody jumped aboard and tried to fire up the engine, but the rising water had flooded the exhaust system and the engine hydraulicked, suffering severe damage. She was repaired at the Marine Depot and spent a short time in Sidney, where I caught sight of her, before being finally sold in 1977.

That was when the *White Pine IV* arrived from Port Alberni, with the intention of ending her days at Prince Rupert. She was a neat little plywood deep-vee with twin 80 h. p. outboards, a sister-ship to the *Salal* and the *Seedling*, built at the Marine Depot in 1958. Already long in the tooth, she was disposed of in Prince Rupert in 1979.

In 1980 a new twenty-foot aluminum boat with a 460 cu. in. gas engine and marine jet unit was custom built and sent to Prince Rupert where, by all accounts, she is performing excellently. It may well be that her light but durable aluminum hull is the answer to the rigours of the log scaling service.

THE BEAUTIFUL SHIP

"She was too fancy. She wasn't practical," Wilf Archer told me.

"She was truly a lovely boat," said Norm Beazley. "Far too good a vessel for the type of work she was doing."

"She was a glory boat," was Hank Doerksen's description.

And Francis Dickie, author, wrote:

"The vessel returned my gaze through the eyes of the beautiful naked figurehead symbolizing all the allure and fatal fascination of those women of ancient Greek myth, calling seductively to mariners to come to their arms. Yet it was the ship itself in my case that was the allure."

They were speaking of the beautiful ship, the *Syrene*.

* * * * * *

She was built in 1921 on the Thames in England, at the yards of John Thorneycroft, for Mr. G. Dragarlis of Ithaca. She was designed for cruising in the Mediterranean and Aegean; and the long, slender lines of her hull recalled the schooners of a bygone era, embellished with bowsprit, scrollwork and figurehead.

But her two masts were not designed to carry a big spread of canvas, and she was powered by twin six-cylinder Thorneycroft engines, for her owner was a practical man.

Her length was seventy feet at the waterline and she drew nine feet. She was narrow, with a beam of little over thirteen feet, the point of maximum beam being well forward. It cannot be denied that in her original form her appearance was a little stark because of the scanty nature of her superstructure. The construction plan and early ph´ t. graphs show a tiny deckhouse amidships, with a low funnel just forward of this. It was as though her designer had exhausted his creativity in planning that beautiful hull.

Construction was teak throughout, with double-planked hull sheathed in copper. On her speed trials she attained 11.08 knots, and she was delivered to her new owner on July 29th., 1921.

Mr. G. Dragarlis, although a Greek millionaire, had amassed his fortune in tobacco rather than shipping. Perhaps because of this he appeared to lose interest in the *Syrene*, or ZEIPHN as her name read in his language. By 1933 she

"She was truly a lovely boat."

was lying abandoned at Cannes, her upper-works grey with neglect and her fine hull streaked with filth.

Enter her saviour, the Reverend John Antle.

* * * * * *

In those days, life on the rugged west coast of British Columbia was hard. Roads were few and air transport in its infancy; so the ocean was the highway for the loggers, fishermen and other hardy people who lived in isolated groups on the edge of the rocky wilderness. The perils of this existence were eased to some extent by the Columbia Coast Mission, who provided medical aid and spiritual comforts.

In 1933 the British Columbia and Yukon Aid Society of England decided to help by providing a suitable boat. They bought the *Syrene*. The Reverend John Antle, missionary, arrived from British Columbia, his intention being to sail her from Cannes to England for a dedication ceremony, then to take her across the Atlantic, through the Panama Canal and up the Pacific coast to her new home. But he had not reckoned with the extent of the *Syrene's* dilapidation.

After weeks of work in Cannes, the vessel limped as far as Gibraltar, where the engines were replaced with Widdop diesels. She called in at Lisbon before finally reaching London in June 1933. Here she was dedicated by the Bishop of London. The *Syrene* became the *John Antle* and was painted black. Now she was ready for her journey . . .

"There's a long account of the voyage of the *Syrene*," John Paynter informed me. "It's on one of the old files." But we looked, and we asked, and the file was nowhere to be found.

Then John suggested I talk to Ivan Teale, one-time cook on the *Syrene* in the days of Captain Bouch. Ivan now had a shore job, but he had kept a few memorabilia of his years on the beautiful ship. Among these were thirteen typewritten pages by an anonymous author, who described himself as 'an axed rubber planter from the Far East.' His account is titled, *'The Voyage of the John Antle.'*

"I was waiting my turn at a barber's shop in the peaceful village of Sunbury-on-Thames," the account begins, "when my friend strolled in and remarked that there lay at Sunbury dry dock a small Mission ship which was fitting out for a voyage to Vancouver, B. C., with a volunteer crew of seven."

After a description of the ship and the fitting out—the ship sailed on July 31st., 1933—the axed rubber planter continues, "Our passage to the Canaries was made in perfect weather, thereby enabling us to discard every garment except a pair of shorts, which became the fashionable wear on board."

At Las Palmas they picked up a piece of human flotsam, "and later we heard from him some details of his roseate past, weird yarns of how he had been in prison in nearly every country in the world, but his passion was voyaging from port to port, taking terms of imprisonment as they came. 'Moving on' was his slogan, and this he declared was the finest life a man could lead."

At Cape Verde Islands they took on more fuel and dealt with a disturbing vibration of the engine shaft. After three days at sea it was discovered that the engines' thirst for oil rivalled that of the Human Flotsam's for alcohol, and the engines were stripped down. New piston rings were fitted. The course was altered for Paramaribo, Dutch Guiana, being the nearest point on the South American coast. "It was impossible to get in touch by radio with other vessels as the dynamo was out of action and the batteries were run down. Added to this, we were out of the usual shipping lanes, in the doldrums, in a dead calm

Bound for Vancouver

HERE is the motor vessel John Antle leaving Greenwich pier on the Thames, bound for Gravesend and the deep blue waters. Inset are Rev. John Antle (left) saying goodbye to Bishop Perrin. Her itinerary is Trinidad, August 31; Colon (Panama), September 7; Balboa, September 9; Manjouillo (Mexico), September 18; San Francisco, October 1; Vancouver, October 6. Originally it was planned to take the North Atlantic route with St. John, Nfld., as the first port of call on the other side of the Atlantic. Several delays, however, caused a start to be made so late in the summer that by the northern route bad weather was to be expected. The voyage is thus made somewhat longer, the total mileage being 10,171.

with long monotonous swells, and a heat that was overpowering."

On August 27th. the ship ran into the first heavy seas they had encountered, and the engine shaft recommenced its vibration. There was very little oil left on board, and waste oil was strained and re-used. At this point we begin to harbour dark suspicions concerning the seamanship of the Reverend Mr. Antle, who elsewhere was described as "a rattling fine sailor if ever there was one." Happily a miracle was at hand, and within a few days land appeared on the horizon. It proved, on closer inspection, to be Trinidad.

On September 16th. they dropped anchor in Cristobal Harbour, Colon, where they enjoyed the distinguished company of the liner *Mauretania*. Two days later they entered the Panama Canal. Arriving at the Pacific Ocean they stayed in Balboa for three weeks while repairs were made. Leaving on October 5th. they headed up the coast and, after encounters with turtles, kelpbeds and friendly Indians reached Long Beach, California on the 22nd. Passage up the California coast was enlivened by a brush with the U. S. Coastguard who mistook the ship for a rum-runner, but sheered off at the daunting sight of the Mission flag.

There followed the roughest weather of the entire trip. "We shipped water which swamped the vessel from stem to stern. We were not far off Destruction Island when it was found that the casting above the port engine had cracked right across, and wdter was pouring into the engine room." They survived this setback too, and on November 14th. arrived in Victoria, B. C.

The epic voyage finally ended at Vancouver on November 20th., some 11,000 miles from the point of departure—and it was here that the generous breasts and suggestive stare of the figurehead troubled the pure souls of the missionaries to such an extent that they decided she had to go. They donated her to the Royal Vancouver Yacht Club—whose soul, we suppose, was beyond salvation—and she now displays her attributes above the Club's entrance at Jericho Beach.

*   *   *   *   *   *

Syrene served as a mission ship for only three years before it became apparent that she was too small for the job. She was sold to the A. R. Williams Machinery Co. of Vancouver, who used her in mining and logging work. Then, in 1938, she was sold to Preston Locke, an American from Pasadena. He lived aboard the vessel in Coal Harbour, Vancouver until he met his death by drowning.

"Carrying top officials on inspections."

The Beautiful Ship

Finally, on August 14th., 1942, she was bought by the Forest Service.

In the early days she plied the coast as the Vancouver Headquarterc launch carrying top officials on inspections. And her name, once again *Syrene*, became inseparable from that of her Master, the redoubtable Captain A. W. Bouch. "He *was* the ship," Jim Sweet told me.

The coast abounds with Bouch stories. The man appears to have made a deep impression on all who met him. Ray Gill, who had been Assistant District Forester at Vancouver, said, "When you went to dinner on the *Syrene*, everybody stood around waiting for Bouch to put on his jacket with the buttons, and until he came and sat down nobody, but *nobody*, sat at the dinner table. He was clean-cut and fairly tall—a striking figure, really. But perhaps we over-did our requirements for a Forest Service captain."

And Tommy Edwards said, "He had a bit of a complex—he thought he was *somebody*. When the *Syrene* came round to the Depot, I remember Art Bouch used to dress up in his gold braid. We'd ask him where he was going, and he'd say some Guild meeting. But he wasn't going to any Guild meeting. He was putting on the dog." Tommy chuckled. "He was a hell of a good skipper, though."

Hank Doerksen had known him over a long period. "Bouch was a real old-time skipper who thought the world of his ship. His deck hand called him 'Sir'. When he came up the coast he'd invite the wives from these isolated stations on board the *Syrene* for tea. His cook, Ivan Teale, would have made all these little pastries and dainties. It was a grand performance, and Captain Bouch would be snapping orders and his crew would be saluting all over the place."

Dignity was the keynote—and dignity is something of an old-world concept. In the easy-going world of the Forest Service it was an anachronism. There never has been a captain like Art Bouch, before or since. Hank acknowledged this, and told of changing times which would eventually bring Art Bouch's career to an end.

"The original idea was that the *Syrene* would be used to transport senior personnel on visits up and down the coast to see that things were being run properly. She was a glory boat, the pride of the fleet. But over the years transport systems modernized, and it became more economical for highly-paid people to travel by air. The *Syrene* began to spend long periods tied up at the dock, and it was thought that she could be put to better use—taking Rangers on timber inspections, for instance.

"Bouch fought that tooth and nail. He was used to taking top officials out. Nevertheless, over the years the *Syrene* became involved in more everyday jobs, like moving Rangers and their families and effects to new stations up and down the coast. Bouch adapted. He would give you the bridal suite for the night, and it became a joke that you made good use of it.

"But he had his rules, and one thing he had a passionate hatred of, was animals on board. Often the young families would have a pet, and dogs had been known to defecate on his teak deck. We'd needle him, too. If there was a move coming up and the weather was good, we'd get all the effects ready. So the M. V. *Syrene* would round the point, and there would be this great mound of furniture on the dock. And we'd sit this wire dog cage on top of everything, so it would be the first thing Bouch saw. It would trigger him off, every time. He'd barely have the line ashore before you'd hear him yelling, 'I'm not taking that bloody dog.'"

In the end *Syrene* became involved in even more mundane tasks, such as transporting planting and cruising crews. Bouch stayed on, jealously protecting his loved one from the rough boots of the Philistines.

And the stories abounded, growing with the years. There was the time he got lost in the fog, and shut down engines as a fishboat loomed up. He took off his jacket with the gold rings and his cap with the gold braid, and laid them on the wheelhouse stool. Then he stepped out onto the deck and hailed the fishboat. "We seem to be a little confused as to where we are," he shouted. "Do you have any idea?" The fisherman gave him his position. So he went back into the wheelhouse, reassumed his jacket, his cap, his role as the omniscient Master, and his course...

Bouch's dress sense irked people; the average Joe has a deep-rooted dislike of uniform. "Captain Bailey backed in the *Bonila Rock* beside the *Syrene*, and up there was Captain Bouch in his jacket, with the gold rings half-way round his sleeves. He looked down at Captain Bailey, who was dressed in dungarees and a tattered old shirt, and he started to shout instructions to him.

"Well, Captain Bailey had skippered ocean liners. He was harbourmaster at Singapore when the Japanese took over. He was at Suva in the Fijis too. And now Bouch was telling him how to tie his boat up.

"So Bailey looks up at Bouch and says, 'Look, mate. When you're entitled to wear those bloody rings all the way round your sleeve, and you've got three more of the bastards on there as well, come and talk to me. Till then, muck off!'"

*   *   *   *   *   *

I said to John Paynter, "I'm getting a one-sided view of Art Bouch. He's an important figure in the history of the boats—after all, he was captain of the *Syrene* for almost a quarter of a century. But I seem to be getting a comic character emerging."

He said, "Talk to Ivan Teale. He was cook on the *Syrene* for years."

Two other things happened. Hank Doerksen recommended Jim Sweet, deck hand, and Doug Adderley of Information Branch reminded me that a dozen of the old *Syrene* log books were available. So I visited Ivan and Jim, and I loaded two boxes of log books into the back of my station wagon, and took them home.

Ivan proved to be an elfin character who'd cooked on the *Syrene* from 1954 to 1972, living on board for thirteen of those years. He had a baker's certificate and had worked in a baker's shop in Ontario. He'd been afloat before he joined the *Syrene*, having served three years on Lake tankers. "I wanted to get away from the water when I came west, but it didn't work out like that. Art Bouch hired me the day I arrived in Vancouver."

At first he thought I wanted to add to my fund of Bouch anecdotes. "I don't want to talk against my captains," he said primly.

"No, I want to know what he was really like."

"He was a very good skipper because he had a standard of work that he insisted on, and he kept the *Syrene* up better than any of the other skippers. We got along very well. He was very punctual—meals had to be right on the dot. I'd do soups and salads, full course meals, desserts, cakes, pies and cookies..."

He talked about the job, mentioning a couple of accidents the *Syrene* had been involved in: a rock struck in Snake Pass, the bowsprit through a fisherman's window at Campbell River. "It lifted the cabin off the fishboat. I was in the galley at the time and I heard the crash and the shouting. The fisherman came out and squawked. Afterwards, they took the bowsprit off." And a time they'd gone aground at Arran Rapids.

The memorabilia he produced were fascinating: old newspaper articles, magazines and photographs featuring the *Syrene*—and, of course, the 'Voyage of the John Antle'. But I'd learned no more about Bouch the man.

"He always stood behind you and backed you up," was all Ivan would say...

In Campbell River I met Jim Sweet and his wife Cecelia.

"Bouch was strict. When I came aboard the ship he said to me, 'I'll show you once. I'll show you twice. The third time—that's *it*.' Any time you tied up, the lines were all put in a coil on the deck. Everything had to be spotless—and I didn't mind that; but I don't know how many gallons of brass polish I went through. It was only after I'd been with him a year that the Old Man let me put a fine coating of oil on the exterior brass."

There was admiration in Jim's tone, but whether for the ship, his captain, or both I didn't yet know. "Once a week I'd do the whole ship from stem to stern. I'd holystone the decks until they were white. I'd wax the engineroom floor until you could see your face in it. If I finished the copper tubing on the engine too soon, the Old Man would come down and scrape some more paint off, so there'd be more copper for me to polish. I even went so far as to vacuum the bilge out."

The discipline extended to navigation. "When I stood my wheel watch I wasn't allowed to sit down. You stood properly at the wheel. You logged every point, every time and course change. He had no time for an auto pilot and he wouldn't even have radar on the boat at first. 'It just leads you into

"The Old Man would come down and scrape some more paint off."

radar-assisted accidents,' he'd say. 'You get to depend on it and you stop using your God-given senses.' I remember coming down Bute Inlet in fog, and the Old Man would blow the whistle. I'd stand outside the wheelhouse and he'd have the window down, and he'd say, 'Count.' When I heard the echo come back he'd know exactly where he was. He'd have every course charted, and he'd always arrive within a minute or two of his estimates. The only instruments he'd use were a compass and depth sounder.

"That impressed me no end, working with a man who was so knowledgeable about things like that."

At last I was getting what I wanted. Cecelia would nod in agreement as Jim spoke. Obviously he'd communicated this admiration to his wife. "He was a fair man," he said. "We'd come in and I'd get the ship cleaned up maybe Thursday afternoon, and he'd say, 'Away you go for the weekend. See you Monday morning . . .'

"And everywhere you went, people would admire the ship. It gave you pride in your work. You'd always get people asking about her, looking at her, wanting to come aboard...Whenever we moved furniture, all the decks would be covered with tarps so they wouldn't get scratched. To me, what's wrong with that? He treated the *Syrene* as though she was his own ship. She was just like a part of him."

I'd called Jim from the Discovery Inn where I was staying, and when I arrived after dinner he'd had time to prepare for me. All the time he'd been on the *Syrene* he'd been writing to Cecelia, and they'd pulled the old letters out and recalled the incidents. "They're love letters, really," Jim said, "but you can look at them if you like." And I said no: I'd rather he talked to me, while I had the tape recorder going.

"I remember once we had a bunch of cruisers aboard," he said. "We were rolling in a heavy west coast swell, while I ferried them back to the ship in a dinghy. It took several trips, and I'd jump out at the beach and hold the dinghy while they got in, so it wouldn't get smashed against the rocks. I'd ferry them back to the ship and drop them off—and there'd be no caulk boots allowed on deck. The guys would take their boots off in the dinghy, climb aboard and put them on the tarp on the deck. Any dirty clothes they had to take off and shake out before they got aboard.

"But what I didn't realize was, I'd lacerated all the backs of my legs on the barnacles on the rocks. When I brought the last of the cruisers in, I climbed up on board. I didn't know there was blood running down my legs—the backs of them were cut to ribbons.

"The Old Man took one look and said, 'Hey, you're messing the deck up!'"

He laughed and poured me a beer. He told me about the time the Old Man had pulled a fishhook from the back of his neck with the engine room pliers, and then he told me about the Snake Pass incident.

"The Old Man should have waited a bit longer for the tide to rise. I was below. The next thing I know the boat gives a jolt and the Old Man rings with the wheelhouse buzzer. I went up and he said, 'We've hit a rock.' And he kept going. He couldn't stop, the pass was too narrow. He said, 'Take the wheel. I'll go below and find out what the damage is.'

"He found he'd cracked two ribs and split a plank, and the water was coming in something terrible." They ran down to Echo Bay that night, and left the engine running all night long, to keep the pumps going. The next morning they ran for Vancouver and put her up on the ways. "The Old Man was sick about that. The boat was his life. He could hardly say a word about the accident."

There was the time they went aground in old Vancouver Bay, at the mouth of Bute Inlet, by the Arran Rapids. Bouch ran out anchors bow and stern and everyone retired for the night. "At one o'clock he came roaring down shouting, 'Get up on deck!' And I found I couldn't get out of bed. The ship had heeled right over and I was on the low side. Ivan was on the high side, and when he got out he fell right on top of me. On deck it was snowing. I rowed around the ship to make sure the water wasn't above the ports, then we all stayed up there for an hour and a half while the Old Man watched his listo-graph. Nobody was allowed to go back to bed until the ship started to come back up—and the Old Man stayed up all night."

He smiled at another memory. "I tried to grow a beard when I was about twenty. The Old Man saw it coming on, and he let me grow it for a while. Then four days later he said, 'Cut it off. It looks shabby. It's a disgrace to the ship.' He always wanted you to look washed and polished, just like the ship.

"And when I was steering he'd come and watch me, then he'd watch the wake. He'd want it straight. *Syrene* was a sonovabitch in a following sea be-cause of that stern—the waves would lift it, and she'd yaw. Other times the Old Man would just sit there quietly in the wheelhouse; maybe he'd say nothing for an hour or more, lost in his own thoughts . . .

"His hobby was carpentry, and one day he bucked his thumb off with the table saw. You know what that old sucker did? He just reached down and picked up the thumb, wiped it off and stuck it back on. His wife took him to hospital and they sewed it back. I admired him. He was one strong-willed old guy. He retired because they wanted him to work on the landing craft, the *L. C. 5*, during the time when the *Syrene* didn't have much work to do. He flatly refused. He wouldn't take another ship, especially that landing barge. To him, that wasn't a ship."

*   *   *   *   *   *

John Paynter filled in a couple of gaps for me. "We presented the original *Syrene* bell to Art Bouch on his retirement. It had the old Greek lettering on it."

I was satisfied with the impression I now had of the captain, and I began to examine the *Syrene's* log books without expecting much further enlighten-ment. Launch log books are usually simple accounts of departure and arrival times, with a sprinkling of meteorological details thrown in.

But Captain Bouch's log books were astonishingly detailed. All voyages were meticulously documented with an entry every time he'd changed course—which often meant an entry every two or three minutes. Courses were detailed, passengers named, and an index at the back of each log showed an alphabetical list of courses steered during the year. More than this, every refit was described in detail showing the daily progress of repairs. All servicing such as topping up batteries was listed. Even when the ship was not in use, the weather for each day was shown.

All this was in Bouch's neat hand, commencing with the historic entry dated August 14th., 1942:

> "Ship purchased from W. C. Mainwaring as is and found and taken over on behalf of the B. C. Forest Service by Capt. A. W. Bouch from Capt. T. Heard. Engines found to need tuning, etc., batteries charged and auxiliaries tuned, and ship in need of clean up, otherwise found to be in excellent condition. Moved to F. B. float in Coal Harbour. .30 minutes—1 mile. (signed) A. W. Bouch."

Small personal notes found their way into the log, too: "March 19, 1943, Feeling ill (2 days) A. W. Bouch."

As did the coming and going of crew. May 6th., 1943:

> "A. Tatlow, cook, gave seven days notice, this date, giving as his reason too much interference from the office. (his opinion)"

Accidents and other important events were recorded in capitals: August 30th., 1943:

> "A. ROBB, COOK, INJURED AT 10.00 P. M. FROM FURNACE BACKFIRE, WHEN TRYING TO RELIGHT SAME WHEN HOT. HANDS, WRIST AND FACE SEVERELY BURNT."

Odd little uxorial details were there. July 12th., 1945:

> "Mrs. AWB aboard."

The first inklings of the jousting propensities of the bowsprit. May 4th., 1946:

> "BOWSPRIT BROKE GLASS IN WHEELHOUSE OF 'SONNY JIM' AT MARBLE BAY."

Crime reared its head on November 2nd., 1947:

"At around 8 p. m. ship was entered by burglars, entry being effected by breaking glass in after window of lounge. Ship was ransacked and burglars escaped, taking with them all silver ware, butcher's knife, paring knife, and ship's binoculars... Deckhand's arrival at 8.30 p.m. probably interrupted burglars. Police notified."

Stormy weather plays its role throughout the log, as witness the entry on March 30th., 1949:

"STRONG S. E. GALE SPRANG UP DURING NIGHT, HEAVY ANCHOR FOULED ON BOTTOM, UNABLE TO RAISE SAME AND HUNG ON UNTIL DAYLIGHT, GALE STILL BLOWING AND DECIDED TO BREAK OUT ANCHOR BY GOING AHEAD UNDER POWER, AFTER TWO HOURS WAS ABLE TO GET ANCHOR ABOARD AND FOUND ONE FLUKE BROKEN OFF AND STOCK BENT."

Famous events are hinted at. October 6th., 1949:

"*Guests*: Mr. G. P. Melrose, Deputy Minister of Lands; Mr. N. DeBeck, Victoria; Mr. W. Huber, Aluminum Co. of Canada Ltd."

Horrifying voyages, such as that of January 12th., and 13th., 1950:

"Towing launch *Oliver Clark*, damaged by fire.
1200 Arr Thurston Bay, fine, light N. Ship covered in 2" ice.
1320 Left Thurston Bay towing *Oliver Clark*.
1530 *Oliver Clark* took sheer in Okisollo Rapids, ramming *Syrene* on stbd quarter and started stem on O. C. also bringing down her foremast. Little damage to *Syrene*.
1600 Pulled clear of rapids and stopped to examine damage and adjust tow.
1615 Under way through Okisollo—very cold—strong N. wind.
1700 Towline froze and broke.
1715 Under way."

The thermometer dropped to zero degrees fahrenheit during the night at Half Moon Bay, and the entry for January 14th. concludes:

"1315 Arr Vancouver. Fraser River frozen—tied *Oliver Clark* at Vancouver float."

Sometimes the passenger list gives cause for fascinating speculation, as on July 22th., 1950:

"Premier Byron Johnson; Mrs. Johnson; Mr. Richards, secretary; Mr. and Mrs. Dawes; Mr. Ray Wormald—Colonist; Mr. Rivers, columnist."

And another viewpoint on a famous tragedy. October 4th., 1950:

"SEARCHED SHORELINE OF BOWEN ISLAND FROM ROGER CURTIS TO HOOD PT, ALSO BOWYER ISLAND AND WATERS OFF ROGER CURTIS FOR WRECKAGE OR BODIES FROM 'A. L. BRYANT' RUN DOWN BY 'LADY CYNTHIA' LAST NIGHT, NO RESULT."

On August 11 th., 1954:

"IVAN WALLACE TEALE, LUNENBURG N. S., HIRED TEALE AS COOK."

A glimpse of another notorious Forest Service incident, on August 12th., 1957:

"MET M. V. BALSAM AND ALDER II AT RENDEZVOUS ISLAND TO ASSIST IN SALVAGE OF WRECKED M. V. DOGWOOD SUNK AFTER STRIKING ROCK."

And a small note on November 1st., 1958: "Mr. and Mrs. Richardson and baby John aboard with furniture for Echo Bay." Nothing could be more at odds with my earlier impressions of Captain Bouch. How many Captains in command of their spotless vessel, dressed in their jacket with rings on the sleeve, would know, or care about, or bother to write down in the ship's log the name of a baby? A new image had finally formed: that of a kindly man doing a hell of a good job, and quite entitled to few idiosyncrasies.

Bouch, a perfectionist himself, clearly expected perfection from others—particularly where matters of marine safety were concerned. On October 12th., 1961 there was a testy note in the log:

"Near collision with M. V. *Atravida* crossing from port to stbd and heading for Texada Island. This vessel failed to give right of way to *Syrene* proceeding to Grief Point. *Syrene* engines put full astern to avoid collision with *Atravida* which did likewise. Both ships stopped with *Atravida's* stem 20 feet from port side of *Syrene*. Three people presumably passengers noted in wheelhouse with Capt. of *Atravida*. I was alone in *Syrene* wheelhouse. This is the second instance involving this vessel which appears to consistently fail to keep a good watch..."

On May 26th., 1962 the Snake Pass incident is reported with the embarrassed brevity of a matter best soon forgotten:

"Current forced ship to port, struck rock, broke two planks on port side below waterline..."

And the night of the grounding, December 1st. — 2nd., 1962:

"Stern aground, listed to 25 degrees, forced on gravel bar by eddies. 1.00 a.m. (Sunday) list 28 degrees. 3.30 a.m. Afloat — no apparent damage..."

The years went by with little incident, and the occasional excitement served only to emphasize the remarkably accident-free record of Captain Bouch. April 13th., 1966:

"BROKE WINDOW OF FISHING VESSEL 'DOCODOMAR' WHEN S.E. GUST THREW BOW OF SYRENE AGAINST IT. OWNER, F. HARTMAN, NOTIFIED."

And so to the sad entry of July 22nd., 1966: "Capt. N. McMillan arrives to take over ship." The chapter ends on July 26th: "Retired as of this date and vessel transferred to Capt. N. McMillan. (signed) A. W. Bouch." And that was all. The last voyage, Blind Bay to the Forest Service Maintenance Depot on July 26th., is listed in the index at the back of the log for the benefit of posterity.

An era was ended.

* * * * * *

So the *Syrene*, now without her bowsprit but with the addition of a stylish cabin and canopy which greatly improved her original appearance, passed to

Neil McMillan, then to Henry McKinnel and on to Norm Beazley, until she was finally sold in 1977.

I visited Norm Beazley in his Vancouver home. Now retired, he was pleased to talk about his career with the Forest Service—he had in fact operated the *L. C. 5* which had so disgusted Art Bouch—and in particular the *Syrene*.

"She was too luxurious, really—all the teak and varnish. And she wasn't all that manoeuvrable—you couldn't twist her round like you usually can with twin screws. She was no hell as a sea boat; in heavy weather the seas would come right over her. You'd never drown her, though—the water would roll right off her. I came across from Cape Mudge in her one time; I don't know how hard it was blowing, but it was nasty. I was running dead slow and Christ, every sea was over her. And she'd roll her heart out in a beam sea, but I wouldn't worry because she'd never hold enough water on her deck to keep her down."

There was affection in her voice. "Other boats I've been on, they'd take that much water and the buggers would sink for a while. But the *Syrene* would come up and just shake her head a little bit, and on she'd go down into the next one.

"I never had any problems with her because I treated her like a lady. I never wanted to harm her in any way because she was that kind of boat—you had respect for the old girl. I liked to see her looking well."

THE HEADQUARTERS LAUNCHES

When the *B. C. Forester* was launched in 1924 she was intended to be a little more than a Ranger launch. She was bigger, her accommodation more luxurious. She was suitable for carrying the top brass of the Forest Service on inspection tours, as well as undertaking the more mundane work of timber administration. She was the fleet's new flagship, deposing the *R. J. Skinner* which was sold in the following year.

She was the first true Headquarters Launch. You have already heard of her building at Thurston Bay, and her rebuilding in 1935. This lengthening coincided with the coming of the *P. Z. Caverhill*, when the *B. C. Forester* was replaced as headquarters launch and turned over to Forest Surveys Branch. When the *Caverhill* was sold in 1941 the *Forester* returned for a couple of years until the purchase of the beautiful *Syrene*.

Lew King captained the *Forester* during her Surveys work. " . . . It was only a summer job. They used to tie the *B. C. Forester* up at Canoe Cove all winter. I took over from Tom Hunter, more or less. There was a temporary skipper but he'd run the *Forester* onto a rock at Tahsis, so they fired him. Meanwhile the boat lay at Tahsis with a timber cruising crew living aboard. They flew me up there and I put her on the beach for repairs. The propeller was all bent so I pounded it back into shape, and we used it like that for the rest of the summer."

He was cautiously complimentary about the ship's handling. "She was a very stable boat; she'd roll quite a bit but never go too far. It wasn't a dangerous roll. It was because of her extra length—she didn't have the beam boats have nowadays. Her steering was good; the controls were very positive. She was well-balanced and I never had any difficulty docking her."

In service the *B. C. Forester* had her share of frightening moments. Like the Blimp *Cherry*, she saw action at York Island. "They had this gunboat you were supposed to report to before you got anywhere near," Lew reminisced. "This night I was coming from Alert Bay to Kelsey Bay and it was storming something awful out there, and I couldn't make any contact. It was getting dusk, blowing, raining. Later it turned out the check boat was laying around the back of the island in shelter. I was supposed to lay out on the other side, but we were rolling terribly, so I kept going. The first thing I knew was a big geyser of water splashing up just a little ways off the bow. Those trigger-happy guys were firing on me!"

The war years brought their special problems. "Late one fall I took F. S. McKinnon—at that time he was in charge of Forest Economics—and George Melrose up to the Charlottes. About the time they wanted to come back, it came on to blow pretty heavy. I didn't want to cross Hecate Strait in that, but after we'd waited a couple of days it began to let up, around noon. They were chafing at the bit, so I said, 'If you fellows want to take a chance, we'll go out a-ways, and if it isn't too bad we'll keep agoing.'

"We kept going, but around four in the afternoon it began to get dark. Long before we got near the coast it was pitch black. There were no lights anywhere on the coast, so the enemy ships wouldn't know where they were. I had to find my way among those rocky shores and up those channels. It was a hair raising experience. As we got closer to shore I could just make out the whiteness of the surf. I was pretty sure where I was, by dead reckoning, and I didn't have any choice but to keep going.

"By ten o'clock I figured I was in the right channel—and I was beat. I'd been at the wheel for ten hours in rough seas. I found an inlet. It was sheltered; the wind was blowing overhead. And there was kelp in there, so I knew there was a fair amount of water. I put her nose right up in the kelp and dropped the hook."

The men pulled out the chart to find out their exact whereabouts. They found the inlet. It was called Murder Cove.

George Melrose, the Assistant Chief Forester, exhausted and sick to his stomach, glanced at the skipper. "Quite a coincidence" he observed sourly.

*　*　*　*　*　*

"The *B. C. Forester* was a lovely vessel," Norm Beazley told me. Norm skippered the ship during her final years in the Sixties, when she was working for Inventory Branch. "She was a good sea boat; she rolled a lot but she was dry. A little slow to stop because she was big for her hundred horse Gardner."

Norm has some stories of life with an Inventory crew. "They were going ashore each day, putting in plots and categorizing the species to get an idea of the make-up of the coastal forest. We had thirteen people living aboard, including the engineer, cook and myself. She was a narrow boat, the *Forester*, and crowded. We had two sittings for breakfast. I'd get up at 5.30 to make sure the cook was available. He was a bit of a boozer, and eventually he went haywire, took a vehicle up to the town and rolled it into a ditch. The party chief fired him and I took over the cooking.

"The first morning, I said, 'You'll bloody well eat what I put down in front of you. The first guy that complains, he's the new cook.' I cooked hotcakes because they were easy, and on the fifth day I heard somebody say,

"'Jesus, hotcakes again.'

"'Who said that?' I asked.

"Not a soul replied. They said I'd imagined it. The loneliness of command. I put up with this for a month before I sent Victoria an ultimatum; either they got a new cook or nobody ate.

"The original cook was a little Scot. He was that much of an alcoholic he could get drunk on one bottle of beer," said Norm admiringly. "On the way back from the Kemano River one day, my engine stopped. There was a hatch in the cabin floor where you dropped down into the engine room. And here's this cook down there—he's shut the engine off, just because he felt like it. I grabbed him by his collar, rushed him into his room and heaved him up into his bloody bunk.

"'If you come out of there I'll ram you right through the bulkhead,' I said.

"'I'll come out if I want to,' he said. But he stayed put."

Eventually the *B. C. Forester* was replaced by more modern craft, and she was sold.

The B. C. Forester *in* 1939, *as rebuilt.*

"The last I saw of her, she was in the Fraser River," said Norm. "A family had bought her, and they were living aboard. She'd be a good ship for that kind of life."

* * * * * *

To me, the *P. Z. Caverhill* had always been something of a mystery ship. I could find no trace of her in the files, which had been destroyed long ago. All I had was the name. "A trifle bizarre," John Paynter said. "It's the Z that does it, I think." And when I mentioned the name to people, they seemed reluctant to talk about her.

In June 1936 the Newsletter contained the following snippet:

"Vancouver District received its newly completed headquarters launch, the *P. Z. Caverhill*, during the past month. The boat is a fine-appearing square stern type of hull, 72 feet in length and with 12 foot 6 inch beam. She is twin screw, powered with two 80 h. p. Atlas Imperial Diesel engines and is capable of a speed of twelve knots, which may be stepped up somewhat when engines and propellers are correctly adjusted. Ac-

"To me, the P. Z. Caverhill *had always been something of a mystery ship."*

commodation includes two double staterooms and bathroom aft, flush deck galley and pilothouse amidships and crew's quarters forward. The Forest Service insignia, in green and white of similar design to our regulation Ranger badge, will appear on her funnel."

A photograph shows her on the ways at Thurston Bay. It does not do her justice. She has a beached and helpless look, and her topsides look vulnerably boxy and oversize.

I tackled Tommy Edwards about her operational characteristics. "One of the officials threw up during a party on board, and lost his false teeth down the head. We had to pull it apart to get them out," he told me.

Although fascinating, this gave small enlightenment on the capacity of the craft to do its job. "She was noted for a yawing problem due to her flat stern," Tommy said.

When I quoted the Newsletter item, he revealed that the *P. Z. Caverhill* was not the innocent virgin I had been led to believe.

"She was an old rum runner. Originally she had three engines: a centre diesel for cruising and the twin Atlasses when she had to make a run for it. She was originally built in Vancouver in 1929 as the *Yurinohana*, Japanese for "Flower of the East." We rebuilt her at Thurston Bay in 1935. A couple of years later she took a sea in Johnstone Strait, and the anchor lifted away and hit the corner of the wheelhouse, and drove it in. We had to repair her."

"What happened to her in the end?"

He seemed uncomfortable. "She was cut in half and sank in 1941. There was some doubt whether she should have been out that day. I don't know too much about it. You might find something in the old newspapers."

Meanwhile Mike Halleran, Forest Service Archivist, had produced another photograph of the vessel; a beautiful shot on a calm sea, showing the *P. Z. Caverhill* at her best. Long and racy she looked; it was easy to imagine her involved in duels of speed with customs launches, knifing through the waves, cutting a V of spray.

In the Legislative Library I found the following item from the *Vancouver Sun,* dated March 7th., 1941.

"3 ESCAPE DROWNING
Forestry Patrol Men Clamber Aboard Steamer

A collision between the C. P. R. SS. *Princess Charlotte* and the Forestry Patrol Cruiser *P. Z. Caverhill* in a fog patch some distance west of First Narrows almost cost the lives of three members of the cruiser crew early today.

Capt. H. C. Alexander was in command of the *Caverhill*, on board which were Ranger E. Hill of Sechelt and Fred Edmond, cook.

They were taken aboard the *Princess Charlotte* and landed in Vancouver, but their abandoned vessel continued during the forenoon to float in the vicinity of Point Atkinson...

Tall, bespectacled Capt. Alexander told the story of the collision in heavy fog to a Sun reporter.

'I was at the wheel,' he said. 'Hill was in the saloon and Edmond was down in the engine room. We were outbound. I saw the *Charlotte* when she was about fifty feet away. We were heading straight for each other and we would have hit head-on if our course had not been changed.'

When Capt. Alexander saw the danger he spun the wheel hard to starboard in a vain attempt to avoid the collision. 'The *Caverhill* shuddered after the impact and started to take water,' he continued. 'It was a lucky thing we were both going dead slow, otherwise our aft end would have shorn off.'

The damaged *Caverhill* was brought into the Vancouver Shipyards plant in Coal Harbour shortly after 1 p. m. where she will be surveyed and repaired."

It was not to be, however. The Forest Service Newsletter later said, "The damage was so extensive that it was decided not to repair the launch. The machinery and equipment were salvaged and the hull sold."

The postscript was added in March 1942. "Jack Scott is down from the Queen Charlottes with the *Lillian D* for the installation of a new engine, which is the 85 h. p. diesel salvaged from the *Caverhill* . . ."

So ended the story of the *P. Z. Caverhill*, or so I thought.

*   *   *   *   *   *

The card index at the Legislative Library showed another entry under 'P.Z. Caverhill' dated June 8th, 1945 in the *Vancouver Sun*. I assumed this referred probably to the man the boat was named after — the Chief Forester who had reigned from 1920 to 1935. Out of curiosity I activated the microfilm machine, and came up with the following astonishing item:

"COLLISION-SMASHED CAVERHILL 'JINX SHIP'
Vancouver trawler, hit by freighter in Straits, has had stirring history

The *P. Z. Caverhill*, 72-foot trawler, which was almost sliced in half early Thursday by an American transport freighter in Straits of Juan de Fuca, today was being labelled a 'jinx' boat as maritime oldtimers recalled the vessel's adventurous background.

The three-man crew of the craft, John Steffich, David Rutka and a third fisherman, miraculously escaped death when the U. S. ship hit them, and Rutka was taken to hospital in Victoria, suffering from exposure. The other two men suffered only minor injuries.

The *Caverhill*, a trim, powerful craft, was formerly a B. C. Forestry patrol vessel, and when one forestry official here was informed of her latest mishap, he said, 'What? Again? She must be hoodooed.'

A few years ago she was involved in an accident almost identical with her latest mishap. In that case she was hit by a coastal passenger ship on her port side, the same side on which she was hit by the American transport vessel Thursday. At one time the *Caverhill* was a rum runner and led a fast and adventurous career in this capacity.

In the latest mishap, crew of the American transport ship rescued the three fishermen, after one or more of them were thrown into the water by the impact of the collision.

The *Caverhill* was severely damaged but not sunk by the crash, and was subsequently towed by naval craft and tugboat to Victoria."

And this time it was the end.

The epitaph was written by the *Victoria Times* on March 21st., 1945.

"Attempts to repair the wrecked otter trawler *P. Z. Caverhill* have been abandoned, Harry Barnett, marine underwriter, said today."

The chapter was finally closed.

* * * * * *

On the North Coast the job of the Headquarters launch and the crew boat overlaps; most launches must necessarily be big in order to withstand the heavy seas of Hecate Strait and other exposed waters. In 1981, for instance, Prince Rupert had a Ranger launch, the *Poplar III*, and a Headquarters boat, the *Hecate Ranger*, which is also used for transporting and accommodating Inventory and other crews around the region.

Probably the first true Headquarters boat in the north was the *Hecate Ranger's* predecessor, the *Salt Mist*.

On January 8th., 1951, Prince Rupert were told:

"We are very pleased to be able to send you word that this very beautifully fitted out boat is going to your District and trust your men will see to it that it is kept in as good condition as it has in the past."

The rough hands and dirty boots of the northern men could not be blamed for what happened next, however, when the *Salt Mist* was sent to Vancouver for strengthening here and there. Red-faced, the Marine Station wrote back on

"This very beautifully fitted-out boat."

May 10th, 1952:

"We regret that the *Salt Mist* will not be ready for service before June 1st. The delay is unavoidable due to the serious rot condition. The first trouble was encountered in the foredeck when we tried to install supporting strongbacks, as it was discovered that the ends of the deck beams were rotten. This necessitated the removal of the foredeck disclosing further rot in the beam shelves, sheer clamps and frame ends."

There followed a progression of disaster. As the examiners crawled aft, patches of rot began to appear everywhere, and in the end the entire deck and a good proportion of the hull were replaced. By the following year, engine problems had begun to surface. "This is the third major breakdown in seven months," said Prince Rupert plaintively. Harry Hill commented on this in a letter to the Chief Forester, Dr. C. D. Orchard:

"... this vessel was built in 1929 as a rum-runner, powered with three 400 h. p. engines and had a service speed of better than 25 knots. During the war she was used by the R. C. A. F. and at that time was powered by a 140 h. p. Vivian, reported service speed of 9 to 10 knots with direct drive... It would appear, therefore, that although we have a hull designed for much greater speed, the present engine does not have sufficient h. p. for continuous running at 8.5 knots with reliability necessary for long open water runs which are at all times necessary in the Prince Rupert District."

She was long, lean and racy, all sixty-eight feet of her, with a high, deep wheelhouse and a long foredeck, and a multitude of windows and ports. She had an air of speedy determination, like a destroyer, as she cut the grey waters with her sharp prow.

But she was not really the right boat for the job. Her hull was too flexible for the rough waters. Because she had the abbreviated keel of a semi-planing boat, she tended to hog when on the ways, and they had to be careful to shore the stern up. "All wooden boats do that," John Paynter told me. "A good shipyard will always uncouple the engine from the propeller shaft before they haul the boat. Then when they launch her again, they adjust the engine mounts so you get a proper alignment with the shaft again. A wooden boat has one attitude out of the water and another in the water. Like a hippopotamus."

The *Salt Mist* added a further dimension to this trait, and matters came to a head one stormy trip when the District Forester was unable to get the pilot house door open due to the flexing of the boat. Justifiably alarmed, Prince Rupert banned her from the Hecate Strait.

In 1961 an ominous note was sounded. "As several years have now elapsed since it was decided the *Salt Mist* was not worth re-engining due to her decreasing age —" At least she wasn't getting any older, apparently "— will you please advise regarding her present condition and her estimated further useful life to the Forest Service."

Shortly afterwards a marine survey reported, "Owing to these defects and considering the age of the vessel it is the opinion of the undersigned that its use should be limited to inside waters in which case the vessel would give a few more years of service."

She was not used again, however. After a period tied up at the Marine Station she was sold to Mr. Ronald E. Ree of West Vancouver in early 1964.

* * * * * *

It was decided that the replacement for the *Salt Mist* would be truly a dual-purpose craft, capable not only of taking officials on inspection tours, but also having sufficient accommodation to handle inventory and other crews.

"I was asked to design a vessel that was capable of operating across Hecate Strait and around the Queen Charlottes," said John Paynter. "She was the biggest boat we'd designed. But then I began to think. If one accepts the fact that there is a storm which can overwhelm any vessel afloat, then one day this storm could overwhelm the *Hecate Ranger*—and people would ask who designed her. So I had my design fully checked out by a professional marine architect."

Rather unkindly, I said, "I understand she has a rolling problem."

"All vessels in that size range react adversely to quartering seas," he said loftily. "In those circumstances she rolls heavily, but that doesn't mean she's top heavy. When I was designing her I wanted to put bilge keels on her, but Harry Hill and Tommy Edwards objected strongly. Later I found out that this was because Tommy was raised in a fishing vessel yard and fishermen hate bilge keels because they tear their nets—so Tommy was brainwashed against them.

"Since the original building in 1962 we've added lead ballast in some quantity. Although Tommy says," he added bitterly, "that he's almost sure that some of the ballast disappeared coincidentally with a time when lead reached a high market value. He suspected that some of it has been replaced with rock."

The *Hecate Ranger* was the biggest boat ever built for the Forest Service, but some would have liked her to be bigger still.

"The Prince Rupert District asked for an eighty foot vessel to cope with the conditions in Hecate Strait and they were probably right, but I knew we didn't stand a dog's chance of getting the money to build that kind of vessel, so we settled for sixty-six feet. I remember the Deputy Minister of the day, Mr. McKinnon, asked me about this, and I said as tactfully as I could, 'All I know is that an eighty foot vessel would have coped a lot better with those conditions than a sixty-six foot vessel, but that hasn't been the only consideration in our design.' We try not to send a boy to do a man's job, but we do sometimes send an adolescent..."

She was fitted with radar and depth-sounder, and even sonar, which the layman might assume was for detecting hostile submarines. "Nothing so dramatic," John said. "The charts off the west coast of the Charlottes are

"It took seventeen years of careful use to justify my original fear."

patchy at best and a forward-scanning sonar enables you to identify a pinnacle of rock before you hit it."

Dramatic enough, though, in those waters. In order to protect her from the worst, the *Hecate Ranger* has a keel and a keelson, with sister keels running alongside the keelson, and a false keel on the bottom. Her keel structure is therefore about four feet wide and four feet deep, T-shaped.

"It took seventeen years of careful use to justify my original fear," said John, "that sooner or later she'd get hung up on a rock."

It happened on July 30th., 1979.

The *Hecate Ranger* arrived at Pearl Harbour, Chatham Sound, towing a helicopter-barge for inventory work on Sunday evening, July 29th., and anchored behind the Flat Top Island because the captain was expecting a westerly wind. After hearing a weather forecast of south-east twenty-to-thirty knot winds the captain motored to a safer anchorage inside Pearl Harbour.

"In the process of moving the boat I had occasion to point out the ominous

top of Datum Rock (now awash) to the man on deck. We then anchored in the lee of the mainland, protected from SE winds," he states in his report.

The ship weighed anchor the following morning at 0500 hours, bound for Prince Rupert. The captain ascended to the flying bridge to observe the streaming out of the helicopter-barge and, satisfied, descended to the pilot house. The promised winds had not materialized and the water was barely rippled, making it impossible to judge the position of the reef in Boat Passage, his most direct route. To make matters more difficult, the radar had not warmed up sufficiently for its signal to be focussed to bring Flat Top Island to bear in relation to the range rings on the screen, so the captain had some difficulty in judging his exact position. He decided it was too risky to attempt Boat Passage, and instead made for Datum Rock Passage, the route by which he had entered Pearl Harbour.

The ship's log then reads:

0510   Struck Datum Rock. Hard aground.

0700   Have made every effort to free vessel but to no avail. Got Fisheries vessel *Petrel Rock* to assist. No results. Vessel heeling badly. Ordered forestry crew to leave vessel. Raised P. R. Coast Guard for assistance on 2182. No tugs in area.

0800   Vince Brown from Rivtow arrived by aircraft. At this time I deemed it necessary to order a salvage barge as vessel was in grave danger.

0930   Search and Rescue vessel *Arrow Post* standing by. Salvage barge en route.

1300   Inspected vessel now completely out of water and resting in a sort of cradle on the rock at 45 degree angle. No obvious damage.

1810   Operations to free vessel commence.

1830   Ship free and making no water other than usual.

1850   Depart Pearl Harbour with barge in tow.

2155   Anchor in Prince Rupert harbour.

It was an unfortunate incident which served to highlight the difficulties in operating on this coast. It also tended to bear out Captain Bouch's contention of some years previously; this was a classic example of a radar-assisted accident. The tide had changed since anchoring the previous evening, giving an entirely new configuration to the seascape. The radar was old, and took too long to warm up. The back-up radar had an idiosyncrasy whereby it displayed a double image at close ranges, and so was not used. And the forward scanning sonar, which in theory would have picked up any underwater obstacle in good time? As the captain said, "Getting under way in confined waters and towing a barge, a captain has plenty on his mind. It's very difficult to assimilate the data provided by more than one navigational aid."

So, running down from the flying bridge to the pilot house after having got under way, he chose the radar because his initial need was to find out exactly where he was. And the radar assisted him to make an error of judgement of a mere ten feet, but enough to put *Hecate Ranger* aground.

There was a thorough enquiry into the incident and it is pleasant to note that the captain was exonerated from blame, as was the helicopter-barge which had been proving so useful for Inventory work on the coast.

*   *   *   *   *   *

The *Hecate Ranger* is a fine vessel of wooden construction. The hull is two inch Douglas fir and the keel and keelson were made by Glu-Lam Products and contribute much towards the strength of the boat. She was designed for use as a waterborne Ranger station, for a floating base for up to eight timber cruisers, and for towing barges. She was built by West Coast Salvage of Vancouver.

She is therefore a little more than a Headquarters boat; in fact by the time of her building the concept of a Headquarters boat had changed. She is a maid of all work, built to operate in rough waters.

One of the nicest stories concerning her work was told to me by Ron Hawkins, who is now the District Manager at McBride. Ron was a green young Ranger at Bella Coola at the time, and learning the ways of the coastal waters. "Use the wind and the tide," he'd hear the tugboat skippers say, as they boasted of their skills in the beer parlours. "Watch the sky, watch the ripples on the surface." And somebody would arrive in town a little earlier than expected, and he'd wink and say, well, I had the wind and the tide with me, you see . . .

"An eye for the weather, and all that stuff," Ron said. "They made a big thing of it, those coast people. I often thought it was aimed at me personally, because I was an amateur."

In those days there was a logger named Mike who had a one-man show up at the north end of Dean Channel. All summer Mike would log, and then he'd sell his logs to the pulp mill. He'd take the proceeds and drink the winter away, then in the spring he'd head on back up Dean Channel to start again. It was a routine existence and there was not much to distinguish Mike from many other one-man shows of his day, except for the dog he had.

The dog could open beer bottles with his teeth. Around noon Mike would lay his chainsaw aside and take up his lunch box, sit on a stump and bring out a bottle of beer. The dog would smile, exposing his teeth. Mike would insert the top of the bottle into the dog's mouth and the dog would take a grip, bracing his legs. Then Mike would lever the bottle down and off would come the cap, and the dog would spit it out and lick his lips, savouring the foam. They were a compatible pair, Mike and his dog.

"One night we were heading up Dean Channel in the *Hecate Ranger*," said Ron. "It was early in the year and pitch black, and we had the radar on. We were just off Mackenzie Rock where Alexander Mackenzie had inscribed his name, when we picked up a blip on the radar, dead ahead. We altered course a bit to avoid it, but it altered course too. We slowed down, and as we watched the screen we realized the boat ahead was going round in circles.

"After a while it appeared out of the darkness—Mike's little tug. Mike was headed up channel to make his fortune again, but he seemed to have gone out of control. We laid alongside and boarded him.

"Mike was lying on the wheelhouse floor, so drunk that he could only see as far as the dog, who was smiling, surrounded by bottle caps. We watched Mike hold out another bottle to the dog, who cracked the cap off, getting in a quick suck before Mike snatched the bottle away. Then Mike realized he had company. He looked up at me, and I think he recognized me. He hauled himself up and scanned the blackness outside.

"'Jeez, I'm making good time,' he said.

"I looked down at him slumped in a rolling, clinking sea of empty bottles, his boat going round in circles in the middle of the night, and I said, 'How do you know that, Mike?' rather sarcastically.

"And he grinned and winked at me, as though I was a kid who knew nothing, and he said,

"'I've got the wind and the tide behind me, that's how.'"

One day in June, John Paynter arrived at my office and asked to borrow some photographs.

"Which ones would you like?" By now I had built up a substantial library of shots of Forest Service boats from all angles.

"Just any photographs. Ranger launches, that kind of thing. The truth is," he admitted, "I've been asked to give a talk on Forest Service marine activities. Really, you ought to be doing it. You know more about the subject than I do, now."

That evening on the Beaver Cove ferry, when he'd told me the legend of Oliver Clark, seemed a long time ago. "The balance of power has shifted, that's all," I reassured him. "Don't let it bother you. You don't know any less than you ever did. It's just that I know more."

"That's true," he said sadly, and departed with a packet of photographs.

The next day he returned them. He was in good spirits; his talk had gone well. "They hung on my every word, Mike," he said. "I held them in the palm of my hand. And afterwards, a fellow by the name of Bob Spearing gave me this."

He handed me an envelope.

"You're going to enjoy this, Mike," he said. "It's a real gem."

＊　　＊　　＊　　＊　　＊　　＊

It was a xerox copy of an article from the *Pacific Motor Boat,* dated June 1920.

"MOTOR BOATS GUARD BRITISH COLUMBIA FORESTS, by W. Bruce Hutchinson.

The sentinels that stand ceaseless guard over British Columbia's vast lumber industry are motor boats; the tireless watchers that protect her priceless timber from the ravages of fire and the wastage of man are motor boats; the eyes of the Forest Service, darting everywhere enforcing the forestry laws—are motor boats; wherever timber borders on water, from the far glassy lakes of the interior to the towering billows of the rocky coast a craft of some kind is constantly on duty."

The article goes on to make several interesting points. The coastline to be patrolled measured over 5000 miles, and the coastal fleet consisted of twenty-five gas-powered boats. There were also a number of open launches on inland lakes, all augmented by hired craft during the 'forestry season'; and 'untold rowboats, skiffs and canoes.'

"Perhaps the most important task performed by the Forestry fleet is the protection of the Province's priceless timber from its great enemy, fire . . . Various regulations framed to prevent the outbreak of forest fires and governing chiefly the work of logging camps have been made by the provincial authorities from time to time. It is up to the forest Rangers to see they are carried out . . . He looks around also to make sure that there is no trespass cutting proceeding on land owned by the Government or private concerns . . . that the logger does not waste the tops of trees or the butts by leaving high stumps . . . the burning of slash must be carried out under the supervision of the Forestry Service . . . with 1429 logging camps working, the Rangers have not been idle and the motor boat engines have not had a chance to rust.

Week after week during the dry season the Rangers are watching for the smoke wreath which betrays the presence of the devouring blaze, ready always to give the alarm.

When he does sight smoke the Ranger makes sure of the location of the fire — and then gives his boat every ounce of gas she will stand, headed for the nearest settlement or camp. About the sparsely-settled coast he may be a hundred miles from any other man save his 'crew'. Worse, he may be absolutely alone and have to sail through heavy breakers, thread dangerous passages and evade frequent rocks. But he keeps on."

New light is shed on some of the boats which, up to now, had been mere names.

"Scalers must be carried about quickly . . . Devoted particularly to this work is the 40 ft. scaler's cruiser *'Gleam'* which was purchased by the service last year.

The particular duty of watching the booms going south and of seeing that they are covered by official licenses is performed by the *'Export Patrol,'* a 20 ft. craft which has been affectionately christened the 'Holy Roller' presumably on account of her tactics in bad weather . . .

The 'Big Three' of the fleet are the cruisers *Red Cedar, Sitka Spruce* and *Douglas Fir* . . . These craft were built at the Thurston Bay repairing station and were constructed on exactly similar lines. Union engines supply the power for all the Big Three, the *Douglas Fir* using 12 h. p. and the other two boats 10 h. p. The mainland coast from Lund north to Knight Inlet is the territory covered by the three sister craft . . .

Away north at Prince Rupert the big 47 ft. cruiser *Uclawtaw*, (*sic*) largest of all the fleet, thunders about under the power supplied by a 50 h. p. Buffalo engine. The *Tempest*, a 40 ft. craft, also patrols the northern shores from Prince Rupert to Masset Inlet on the Queen Charlotte Islands. Prince Rupert . . . also has the *Embree*, a 30 ft. cruiser powered with a 20 h. p. Union engine . . . "

This is the only mention of the *Tempest* I have come across. No details have come to light on her size, engine or appearance. The next mention is of more familiar craft, though.

"One of the finest boats in the fleet is the *Leila R* . . . She plies between Prince Rupert and the Queen Charlotte Islands, a territory in which a boat which can stand anything is needed.

The *Beatrice R* and the *Eunice B* are a pair of cruisers which differ only in the shape of their cabin tops . . . Queen Charlotte Sound, a wind-swept water north of Vancouver Island, is the sphere of the *Beatrice R's* activities, while the *Eunice B* patrols the mainland and the East Coast of Vancouver Island from Rock Bay to Port Hardy. The *Eva R* and the *Geraldine R* are craft of the same model . . .

A real old-timer, named after the first B. C. forest Ranger, is the 45 ft. *Skinner* . . . She holds the distance record for the fleet, for she had travelled 60,000 miles and, with her 35 h. p. Buffalo engine, is still standing the strain.

At Lund hovers the 40 ft. *Alanbee* which is powered with a 24 h. p. Union engine. At Pender Harbour the *Kiora* is on the job, while sailing out of Vancouver is the cruiser *Aleli* powered like the *Kiora* and *Alanbee*.

The northern part of Vancouver Island is patrolled by the *Idonno*, a 32 ft. craft powered with a 15 h. p. Corliss engine. She has a comfortable cabin forward and a roomy cockpit aft.

The *Nerka* . . . patrols Cowichan Lake . . . On Toba Inlet the open launch *Kay* is being operated. On Powell Lake is the little *Jean L*. On

Harrison Lake further inland is the open *Mac*. In the centre of the province the *Adam Lake* patrols Adams Lake. Besides these there are several rowboats propelled by stern engines" (which the article elsewhere refers to as 'overboard' engines) "while the number of skiffs and canoes is legion."

There were photographs also: The *Leila R* at speed, the *Eunice B* and the *Beatrice R*, the *Geraldine R* in a sunset shot, the 'Big Three,' the *Skinner* looking gaunt and weatherbeaten, and the only photograph I have seen of the *Idonno*.

A gem indeed.

* * * * * *

Then, as now, one of the most important Forest Service tasks was fire suppression, and one day I visited Don Owen, the retired Director of Protection Branch, to talk about this aspect of operations. It was a damp morning in May but it was cheerful in Don's living room, drinking coffee and talking about boats. Like many Forest Service bosses, Don had worked his way up through the ranks. Early in his career he was posted to Pender Harbour and, naturally enough, enquired about the sailing times of the Union ship.

"Oh, no," they told him. "You're going to take the launch."

"But I've never taken a boat up the coast before."

"That's all right," they assured him. "We'll hire an engineer."

They hired the next man who walked into the Marine Building. He was warm. He was moving. He was a big blustery man by the name of Walter.

"You know the coast?" asked Don anxiously.

Walter did. He'd been up to Alert Bay, ten years ago, in a fishboat. He was sure it had been Alert Bay.

"Do you know where Pender is?"

Walter was damned sure he could find it.

So they went to the Marine Station and met Bob Swan, who was to instruct them in the mysteries of the *Hemlock*. Bob piloted them away from the dock up to the mouth of the Fraser.

"Now you take her back," he said, "and we'll make a landing at a boom on the way."

So Don drove them back. He avoided colliding with outgoing tugboats, and laid the *Hemlock* alongside a boom without springing the planking, and

"You're going to take the launch."

finally docked at the Marine Station. Bob Swan was delighted.

"Fine," he said. "You're all ready to go."

"What?"

"Well, tomorrow morning, then. I can't see you having any problems."

At six-thirty the next morning Don and Walter set off. The Fraser was calm enough, but once they got outside the mouth all hell broke loose. There was a Squamish blowing and the tide was running fast. The sea was lumpy and the pounding of the Gardner diesel was augmented by the crash of Don's furniture tumbling about below.

"I suppose this is about normal for the time of year," said Don lightly.

Walter agreed that it very probably was. Off Bowen Island, however, it seemed that matters were getting out of control. The wheel had a will of its own and Don kept finding himself treading air, the deck having dropped away from under him. He handed over to Walter, who was more heavily built, and tried to rope a few things down to increase the safety factor in the wheelhouse. With everything secure, he wedged himself into a corner and scanned the heaving seas.

"I guess we should head on up the channel, now," he said.

Walter asked which channel.

Don searched for a chart. There was no chart to be found. There was, however, a road map of the Province, published by an oil company. It appeared to be part of the boat's standard navigational equipment, and Walter assured Don that he always made a point of buying that particular company's gas. Pender was not marked, but Gibson's was, and it was not too far off, either.

As they passed the western tip of Bowen Island the wind eased off and the seas dropped a little, and Gibson's lay ahead, looking extraordinarily inviting. Don aimed the *Hemlock* in that direction.

"There's not much room in here," he said nervously, as they approached a phalanx of fishboats twelve-deep at the dock.

Walter was of the opinion that the dock was crowded because the fishermen were striking for better prices and the closing of waters to American sports-fishermen. Don began to worry about his ability to make a clean landing in front of the experts. Fifty feet off the nearest boat, he cut the engine and got out paddles, and the two men sculled cautiously in. The fishermen watched with interest, calling their mates up from below. Soon a crowd had assembled, murmuring excitedly. There was scattered applause and the barking of dogs. Somebody shouted:

"Here comes the Forest Service!"

Don and Walter tied up beside the nearest fishboat. They were helped on board, and clapped on the back, and offered hot coffee. There was a heady air of masculine bonhomie and goodwill. Gazing down at the tiny *Hemlock*, one of their new friends said:

"I sure admire you guys—we've been stuck here two days. Only the Forest Service would have the guts to go out in weather like this!"

* * * * * *

"One of the biggest problems in Forest Protection in the Vancouver Region was fires in the inlets," Don said. "You'd spot a fire from a distance and you'd take the boat up as close as you could. Then you'd try to develop your strategy for fighting it—but you'd find you didn't have a landing barge to bring a Cat in. We've had to move Cats on log floats and all kinds of weird things.

"I remember we had a fire once on Crown Zellerbach's operation up Tribune Channel. The fire was all over the hillside, fully visible from the launch, but before we could do anything about it we had to run four miles up the inlet and find a safe place to anchor the boat and get ashore, with beaches few and far between. The Brittain River fire in 1951 started from a lightning strike on the mountain top, and it took Denny Allison and his crew eight hours to walk into the fire. There were five of them and they were loggers and damned good bushmen, but by the time they'd climbed from water level to a point 3500 feet up the hillside that was their day; they couldn't do any more."

He frowned, remembering. "The next day they started to work on it — but the wind came up and boy, that fire jumped from the mountain peak on one side of Brittain River over to the other side, and the whole bloody valley just exploded. Manpower in those circumstances is absolutely useless. Nowadays we have helicopters, air tankers and all kinds of things which speed up the initial attack.

"Most Ranger launches would carry a pump and 1500 feet of hose, together with hand tools for eight to ten men. And you'd be alone on the boat, so you were dependent on who you could recruit. People would co-operate, though, because they were interested in looking after their own resources. A guy would be logging nearby and he'd spot a fire and think — hey, maybe I'll be wanting to log that timber some day. We looked on it as our responsibility to maintain good relations with the people in the inlets, although sometimes we had to tread a fine line. We'd be reaming a guy out for trespass one afternoon, and later we'd be having supper with him. And we had an honorary fireward-en organization, which meant we had a responsible person in each inlet."

The *Hemlock*, Don's first boat, had been added to the fleet in 1925. She was a forty-foot double-ender built by Mortimer and Knight, with a nine foot six beam and drawing three foot four. She had a reputation for rolling in beam seas.

"The *Hemlock* was top-heavy to start with," said Don. "She was like an oversized canoe with a house on top, and in any kind of sea she'd submarine along, taking it right over the pilot house. She was worst in winter, though. With slushy wet snow that's freezing you can pick up a load of ice in no time and boy, that's scarey. You can roll over so fast you wouldn't know what hit you."

Frank Tannock had experience of the *Hemlock* when he was Ranger in Port Alberni.

The Ranger Launches—I

"We nearly lost her one night across from Sarita. We were tied to an A-frame logging show; the logging crew were commuting to Port Alberni, so there was nobody there but ourselves. A howling wind came up out of Sarita, straight across the channel . . . "

It stripped the corrugated iron off the donkey shed and whirled it away like leaves. Then a boom of logs broke loose and bore down on the *Hemlock*, heaving menacingly in the swell.

"Logs were going underneath the *Hemlock*, and she was crashing down on them fit to knock the bottom out of her. We'd climbed out onto the A-frame by then—some captains may believe in going down with their ship, but not me. We were able to pull the bow into the shelter of the A-frame, but the stern still stuck out. We fought that storm for a good hour, trying to fend off the logs, before the wind died down . . . "

She may have had her handling problems, but the old *Hemlock* was solidly put together. When the men cleared the last of the logs away and examined the hull, there was no damage except for a few dents. At midnight they headed out to find a more sheltered mooring.

*   *   *   *   *   *

You have already heard of the 1925 launching of the *Oliver Clark*, *Hemlock's* sister-ship, by Miss Doris Pattullo, and the uncomplimentary view of her performance as expressed by Wilf Archer. We must remember, though, that standards improve just as steadily as boats age, so that the older boat in present-day service has two strikes against it. "Talk to Arnold Ginnever," Don Owen said. "He was on the old *Oliver*." Arnold is retired from the Forest Service now but I caught him at the Forest Protection offices one day, and sat him down with the tape recorder.

"I arrived at Thurston Bay in July 1949, as a new Ranger, and found the *Oliver Clark* sitting there, forty foot long. I'd never operated anything bigger than a rowboat before, so my first job was to learn how to run the boat. The other Ranger at Thurston Bay ran the *Forest Ranger II* and he was quite accomplished, but he wasn't about to pass his knowledge on to the new boy. So I leaned heavily on my engineer, Stuart Smith. He's dead now."

With Stuart as his mentor the young Arnold soon grasped the rudiments —except for one thing.

"I couldn't make starboard landings. On the old *Oliver*, as with many boats, when you come into dock you go astern and feed the power to her, and she'll draw in to port. That's fine if the dock is on your port side. Often it isn't.

"On one occasion I came into a logging camp at the mouth of Phillips Arm. It was a floating camp surrounded by boomsticks, and there was a gap about one boomstick in length, that the boats went through. I saw a big tug tied up there, and another boat behind it. There was just enough room to dock the *Oliver*—on a starboard approach.

"'I don't think I can make it,' I told Stuart.

"'If you don't, you'll never learn,' he said."

So Arnold aimed the *Oliver Clark* at the dock. When he was twenty feet away, a gust of wind swept across the water. The boat drifted off course. Arnold groped for the clutch wheel, which was behind the operator as he stood at the helm.

Now the wheel in the old *Oliver* had an odd little quirk. In appearance it was perfectly normal; a wheel mounted on a vertical shaft; the rim of the wheel horizontal with the words AHEAD and ASTERN stamped on it. But some mechanic in the dim past had hit upon a way to keep the boat's operator on his toes: the wires beneath the deck were crossed.

Of course, Arnold knew that ASTERN meant AHEAD and vice versa, but in the excitement of that moment at Phillips Arm he forgot. Glancing behind him, he twisted the wheel to ASTERN and felt it click into position. Then he poured the throttle to the old Vivian engine, intending to bring the boat to a rapid stop. Instead the *Oliver Clark* bounded forward, caromed off the side of the tug, porpoised over a half-sunken boomstick and came to rest lying comfortably up against the camp cookhouse. The only damage was to Arnold's ego, as the camp cook shrugged his shoulders over this unusual method of landing, as though to say that it was no more than he would expect from a Forest Service landlubber.

"So you didn't care much for the old *Oliver Clark*," I said, recalling Wilf Archer's scathing comments.

He corrected my impression quickly. "She was a really good boat, and I got to like her. Mind you, everybody else laughed at her because she was old, and she had her little peculiarities. When you were running you couldn't leave anything on the table; the vibration from the old Vivian would have it on the floor in seconds. The whole boat used to shiver. But she was a double-ender—very good in a head sea and on the quarter, and she was relatively easy to handle in a following sea, which is something you can't say for a transom stern. She rode the sea like a duck. She'd take anything up to eight foot waves without any problem. I liked her," he repeated honestly, "and old Stuart Smith, God rest his soul, he liked her too."

Arnold told me of other adventures that summer; of the time he fell between the *Oliver Clark* and the wharf one night, while Stuart was docking the boat in a three-foot slop: "I thought: my God, I'm going to meet my Maker now. I'd hit my ribcage on a projecting plank and I was kind of hurting. But somehow I managed to scramble out before the old *Oliver* crunched up against the float." He told stories of Bute Inlet, where a trip to the head of the inlet would take the best part of a day, if you caught the tide wrong. Running through these wry stories, like a counterpoint, was his love for the boat.

"I'm not kidding you, Mike, when you walked into the *Oliver Clark* it was just like turning back the clock twenty-five years. There was brass everywhere and old Stuie used to keep it all shined up. There was no such thing as plywood panelling; it was all three-eighths V-joint. She was just beautiful."

Disaster came in the winter of 1949-50.

The snow was up to their shoulders at Thurston Bay. Arnold and Stuart and their families were the only inhabitants that Christmas, so they drank together on Christmas Eve and eventually went to bed. During the night another thirteen inches of snow fell. On Christmas morning Arnold and Stuart set to work shovelling the boardwalk clear. By noon they'd worked their way down to the floats and shovelled them off, then they started work on the decks of the *Oliver Clark* — an important job, since the boat was already unstable with the weight of snow. Arnold was shovelling off the foredeck while Stuart cleared the cockpit. He heard Stuart open the after door. Then:

"Good God, Arnold — come and look at the boat!"

The entire interior of the *Oliver Clark* had been gutted by fire. The beautiful V-joint panelling was now charcoal. The cables were hanging loose and bare, and there was melted lead spattered over the floor. The electrical panel was destroyed, the main cabin and the galley were black stinking shells. Thick black smoke had congealed on the deckhead into a waxy soot.

"As we reconstructed the fire afterwards, the wick-burning oil stove had flooded during the night and caught fire. We used to leave it on to keep the boat aired. Anyway, in the end there must have been so much smoke in there that the fire smothered itself."

In early January Arnold got a radio message to say that Captain Bouch would be arriving at Thurston Bay with the *Syrene*, to tow the *Oliver Clark* down to Vancouver. Arnold would stay aboard the *Oliver Clark* to steer.

"Art had decided to go down Okisollo Channel and through Surge Narrows, and down there you could run into some pretty big eddies. It was bitterly cold in the old *Oliver Clark* and I knew those guys in the *Syrene* would be sitting in the warm, drinking coffee. I wasn't feeling too pleased about this. It was a brilliantly clear day, but the temperature was around zero."

Something nudged at my memory. "This wasn't the year the Fraser froze over, was it?"

"That was the year. It was the worst winter we had in years."

"I read about that trip in the old log of the *Syrene*. I've already mentioned it in the *Syrene* chapter. It would be interesting to hear it at first-hand."

So he told me. It was the time of big tides, and they rode the flood through Okisollo Channel, through turbulence, over falls and whirlpools. All went well until they reached the Hole-in-the-Wall, where they encountered a strong outflow and winds around 35 m. p. h. blowing down from Bute Inlet. The Hole-in-the-Wall is famous hereabouts; you can get a six-foot overfall on high tides.

As luck would have it, this was the place where the *Syrene* ploughed into the fiercest whirlpool they had encountered. Slowing perceptibly, she fought the current.

But the *Oliver Clark*, helpless without power, slid the other side of the whirlpool. She accelerated.

"She was completely at the mercy of the towline — and she was really straining at the end of it, heeled so far over with the sideways pull that I was sure she'd capsize. She skittered around the other side of that eddy like a roped bull. I saw the *Syrene* loom up at me; the *Oliver* was charging straight for her side in the basic ramming approach. Then — crash! It tore a great big hole in the rubbing strip of the *Syrene*, and it completely separated the stem of the *Oliver* from the planking."

"What was Bouch's reaction?"

He smiled ruefully; the memory was still clear. "He was very upset. He came out of his wheelhouse and looked down at the damaged side of the *Syrene*, and there was a kind of sick horror on his face. He wasn't concerned about the *Oliver Clark*, even though she was in danger of going down, with the bow all split apart."

"So how did you fix her?"

"The weather did that for us. The water was turbulent and the wind was strong, so there was a lot of spray. Every time the spray hit, it froze. Pretty soon it had plugged the bow of the *Oliver* with ice . . . ”

Their problems were not over, though.

“Art took pity on me, and we lashed the wheel of the *Oliver* and I went aboard the *Syrene*. We had a cup of coffee and set off again. We went through Surge Narrows without incident. We were all in the wheelhouse passing the time of day, when I suddenly thought: by golly, I’d better go out and check on the old *Oliver*.

“I went around to the stern of the *Syrene* — and there was no *Oliver* there . . .

“There was just a little piece of towline, about two feet long, hanging over the side. What had happened, the line had got soaked and frozen, and you know how brittle frozen lines are. So we put about and headed back, and after a while there she was, bobbing up and down on the water. Anyway, we finally got her to Vancouver, only to find the Fraser was frozen over. So we had to sit in the harbour for a week or so.”

That was the last Arnold saw of the old *Oliver Clark*. They rebuilt the interior and replaced the blackened V-joint with more modern panelling, and sent her back on her way with a 6-cylinder Chrysler. Arnold took the *Alpine Fir II* back to Thurston Bay.

*   *   *   *   *   *

“Remembering Arnold and the old *Oliver Clark* reminds me of something,” Don Owen said, pouring me another coffee. “You’re familiar with the legend of Oliver Clark the man, I suppose.”

“I’ve heard it.”

“Well, back in ’42 I was a dispatcher at Invermere, working for Ralph Johnston — he retired as Regional Manager at Kamloops in 1979. One day I happened to be rummaging under the counter and I came across this fire file. I got to reading the fire history — and here was this account of the fire written by a chap named Barney Johnson who was a Ranger in that area. Barney was quite good at dramatizing a story and it read well. There were long, vivid passages culminating in Oliver Clark’s body being found against the log with his Forest badge clutched in his hand.

“However, Barney Johnson was nicknamed ‘Ninety-Nine Year Barney’ because somebody had once calculated that if he’d lived through all the experiences he said he’d had, he’d already be ninety-nine years old. He was Ranger at Invermere two years before I got there, and I suppose he was so pleased with his account of the fire that he kept the file. I can't think of any other reason for it being at Invermere — it's a long way from Port Neville."

Later I was able to find a reference to Ninety-Nine Year Barney in the Forest Service Newsletter of January 1st., 1941.

> "*F. J. G. (BARNEY) JOHNSON*
> Born in London, England. His wife and family are living in North Vancouver. Was first employed in the Service as Assistant Ranger at North Vancouver in 1931 and continued in that position until 1937, when he was appointed Ranger at Thurston Bay. Was transferred to Invermere in the Nelson Forest District in 1939, where he remained as Ranger until leaving the Service in 1940."

Barney then enlisted, and was last heard of as 'second in command of a corvette.' In a poignant letter, he says, "And now may I again thank you and the Service for remembering me, and ask you to please not forget to send the News Letter, for I miss the 'outfit' terribly much."

So Barney Johnson had joined the Forest Service six years after the death of Oliver Clark, and had never, apparently, been near Port Neville. I was left wondering why he had written the account of the incident. Could it have been for a published article? If it was, I was never able to locate it.

* * * * * *

In 1925 the last of the larger boats which was to serve the Forest Service through the Twenties and Thirties was built by the Prince Rupert Dry Dock Company. She was the *Lillian D*, a solidly built sixty-footer intended for use around Prince Rupert and the northern coast. A succinct summary of her early work appears in the Newsletter of March 1942:

> "Jack Scott is down from the Queen Charlotte Islands with the *Lillian D* for the installation of a new engine, which is the 85 h. p. Atlas Imperial Diesel salvaged from the *P. Z. Caverhill*. The old engine, a Petters semi-diesel, carried Jack 150,000 miles in the last 17 years. Same man, same boat, in some of the toughest waters on the coast. Hecate Strait, Dixon Entrance, west coast of Queen Charlotte Islands, as well as the ticklish waters around the mouths of the Nass and Skeena Rivers. From the appearance of the *Lillian D* one would never suspect she had been through so much."

154

"She was the Lillian D.*"*

In search of further information on this boat I talked to Hugh Bancroft. Now retired, the mild-mannered Hugh had worked in the Prince Rupert area in the early Fifties.

"They sent the *Lillian D* to Ocean Falls in 1949 to replace the *White Cloud* which caught fire and sank that year. I joined her in 1951; we had the *White Birch* there too — she was used by the assistant Ranger in the summer."

He went on to describe an incident in the fall of that year.

"At four in the afternoon I got a telephone call that there was a fire down at Rivers Inlet. It was an eight-hour trip, so we decided to get some sleep and start out at two in the morning, so we could find somewhere in daylight to tie up. We put a fire pump on deck.

"In the middle of the night we were chugging down the channel, barely able to make out the shore on either side. We shouldn't have been travelling really; and at one point we heard a thump — we'd hit a deadhead without seeing it. Neil McMillan and I were alone on the boat, in the wheelhouse."

So they motored on in the darkness, and later Hugh went below to make coffee.

"There was a foot of water in the galley! I rushed back up and told Neil to cut the speed while I took a closer look down there to find out what had happened."

Water was pouring in through the stuffing box. Obviously the deadhead had done more damage than they'd realized. They started up the bilge pump, but the water level continued to rise; the pump couldn't keep pace with the inrush. They wondered what to do. It was too dark to beach the *Lillian D*; they could barely make out the shore and could have easily run the boat straight onto a rock, or worse, into a cliff face. The water level was rising rapidly. The situation was desperate.

"So what did you do?" I asked. "Take to the lifeboats?"

He smiled gently. I'd forgotten what John Paynter had told me. They were resourceful men.

"We had the fire pump on deck, remember? We rigged up the intake down in the galley, started it up, and kept it running until daylight. That kept the water level down. Then we beached the *Lillian D* at an old fishing boat grid at the top of Rivers Inlet, and pumped her dry with the falling tide. I got a fishboat and went to take a look at the fire, leaving Neil in charge of the boat. By the time I got back, he had some bolts into that stuffing box and we were able to limp back to Ocean Falls."

I was visualizing the scene; the darkness, the sinking boat. "But suppose you hadn't had the pump with you?" I said.

He smiled again. "I daresay we'd have thought of something," he replied.

*   *   *   *   *   *

I found an old file dealing with the *Lillian D's* later years, at the back of a cabinet in the Maintenance Depot. In 1951 she was rebuilt from the decks up and the engine replaced. She ran without incident until 1956, when she sustained damage as a result of being rammed by the towboat *Sea Queen III*. In 1962 the first sounds of her impending end were heard: a list of defects from her new captain.

"The fuel tanks of this vessel are in horrible shape. The filters are filled with black scum and consequently I figure they are unsafe for further running." There followed details of leaking decks, rotting woodwork and a host of other major and minor faults.

The work was completed, but in January of the following year, the captain reported:

"Arrived at Standard Oil, 1430 and commenced taking fuel and water . . . As

"In 1951 she was rebuilt from the decks up . . . "

I started to put gas in anchor winch tank an explosion took place in the fore-castle of the vessel which resulted in a fire."

Later the Marine Superintendent, Harry Hill, reported: "The fire (explosion) was caused by a defective gasoline tank under the deckhead in the chain locker, the fumes travelling aft until they were ignited by the furnace in the room behind the forecastle . . . "

Again she was repaired and put back in service, but on November 19th. there appears a quotation from the Propellor Repair Shop, Ltd. of Vancouver,

"1 only 41 by 21 3 blade Osborne Manganese Bronze Propellor, pitched and balanced . . . $337.00

And handwritten beneath, a note from a Forest Service Officer:

"Tom Edwards—too much and too late, for your info."

On April 5th, 1965, the *Lillian D* was sold to Mr. M. G. Troop of Sidney, B. C.

*   *   *   *   *   *

Another boat which saw service in the mid-coast area around that time was the *White Spruce II*. Built as an air-sea rescue launch, this thirty-seven foot wooden craft was originally called the *Hurrier*. John Paynter himself took delivery of the boat in 1955 at Maple Bay, where the marina operator showed him the pushbutton system for changing gears from ahead to astern.

Fully briefed and feeling confident, John and the *Hurrier* raced across the Gulf and up the Fraser, and in due course the Maintenance Depot loomed ahead. Steering for the dock, John prodded the reverse button.

Nothing happened.

The *Hurrier* bore relentlessly on. By now she was in the narrow confines of the dock complex, and it was impossible to turn. Ahead lay the gleaming stern of a Blimp, freshly painted from a complete refit. On the dock stood the redoubtable figure of Harry Hill, then Superintendent of the Depot. Groaning with despair, John beat a tattoo on the button.

The *Hurrier* ploughed on with a bone in her teeth, a fine sight. The gleaming stern ahead carried the name *Douglas Fir II*, each letter of which was becoming burned into John's optic nerves. It was a sunny day in 1960 with a slight chop, visibility good.

The *Hurrier* demolished the rear end of the *Douglas Fir II*.

And then there was the gathering of spectators like hyaenas at the kill, and the hellfires of embarrassment, and the expression on Harry Hill's face...

"I was informed that there was a Bendix involved somewhere in the mechanism," John said sadly, "and you had to hold your finger on the button until the gear cut in. I didn't know that at the time. Naturally enough, I was stabbing at the damned thing frantically—and that was the wrong thing to do..."

So they repaired the *Hurrier*, repainted her and named her the *White Spruce II*, and sent her north.

"I got her around 1961 at Bella Coola," said Ron Hawkins. "She had a flat bottom with twin engines for rushing to the scene when an aircraft crashed at

"The Hurrier *bore relentlessly on."*

sea. She was probably very good at it, too, but she was a poor boat for Ranger work on the coast. She was a real dog in any kind of a sea. I needed a fast boat, because I had a huge district to cover with long, narrow inlets. But with the *White Spruce II*, if it was rough I couldn't go out."

* * * * * *

I'd had a very interesting discussion with Don Owen which had left me with a full tape to transcribe later. As I left his house I was thinking how fortunate I'd been to have chosen the Forest Service as a subject for this, my first non-fiction book. Forest Service men tend to be articulate and accustomed to public speaking, and are not thrown off balance by the sight of a tape recorder revolving relentlessly at their elbow. They've lived interesting lives and they know how to talk about it.

Don's last words stayed with me as I drove home; they were a suitable epitaph to a career spent guarding the forests against the inroads made by man and nature.

"It's very gratifying to see the old places now," he said. "I remember going into Vancouver Bay when they were logging out the back end—Jesus, it looked a mess. Then as time went by I saw the second growth coming in. Now it's completely regenerated as a second-growth stand. And Brittain River was all slash for the first six miles, but it's come back now.

"It's good to see that. It makes me feel my work has been an important part of the growing-up of the Province, and it gives some meaning to all those years I spent with the Forest Service."

John Paynter was born in 1921.

"A vintage year," he told me, "which saw the building of the *Syrene* and other great events. My father bought me a canoe at the age of ten, and I got into sailing during my teens. Ever since then, I've always had a small boat, maybe two or three."

"Why always small boats?" I asked.

"Because I know how much it costs to maintain large boats," he said grimly. "Then later I was apprenticed at Vospers, who specialized in wooden vessels at that time. Wood has always been my particular joy, and I was very lucky to get in at the twilight of the wooden shipbuilding era.

"Vospers built motor torpedo boats and other fast wooden craft—I even worked on Sir Malcolm Campbell's *Bluebird*, the one which broke the world's water speed record in 1939 with a speed of 130 m. p. h. When the war got under way I joined the air-sea rescue service, but pretty soon they found that I was experienced in the shipyard aspects, and they took me off the water and put me in maintenance."

John arrived in Canada in 1946, and it so happened that the Forest Service was looking for someone with his capabilities at that time; someone who knew about wooden boats and their idiosyncrasies.

"All the Forest Service boats were wooden. This was partly an act of faith on the part of the Ministry because we were in the wood business," he smiled, "although they hadn't carried it to the extent of building wooden cars. The Minister of the day, Mr. Williston, said to me, 'John, we should always be seeking to demonstrate the continuing advantage of wood as a shipbuilding material.' We took it too far in the end. By the time we built our last wooden vessel, the *Coast Ranger*, the fishboat and tugboat industry had swung over to other materials and we had to go down on bended knee to the lumber industry and beg for yellow cedar to plank her."

But meanwhile, John had inherited a fleet of solid timber vessels, full of character, beautiful to see.

* * * * * *

The Ranger Launches — II

You have already heard that no boats were built by the Forest Service during the Depression years. The old Ranger launches soldiered on, each year getting a little more weary, sustained only by the excellence of the maintenance work at Thurston Bay. Then, shortly before World War II, a trickle of new recruits entered the ranks. In 1937 the *Nesika* and the *Forest Ranger* were bought, and in the following year the *Wells Gray* and the *Tamarack*. In 1939 came the ill-fated *Dogwood*, in 1942 the oriental *White Cloud*. Then shortly after the war, the *White Spruce*, *Maple* and *Balsam*.

*   *   *   *   *   *

I saw the old *Nesika* in 1982, and she was a sad sight. Paul Stenner had invited me to take a look at the *Wells Gray*, which he bought from the Forest Service in 1979. The *Wells Gray* was lying at Canoe Cove Marina, resplendent in a new coat of paint, and while I was admiring her my gaze fell, as if seeking a contrast to this glory, on an ageing, unkempt craft of similar size nearby.

It was the *Nesika*. Now owned by the Federal government she had clearly fallen on hard times. Her paintwork was peeling, her brightwork dull, and thick green tendrils reached from her bottom towards the ocean floor as though seeking to draw her to a timely grave.

Forty-five years is a long time for a wooden boat.

"An opportunity to pick up a real bargain occurred and the Scotch in us came to the top, so we bought the 48-foot diesel yacht '*Nesika*.' This is one of the best-built private boats we have seen and has been placed in the northern ranger district under Vancouver. Ranger Langstroth at Port Hardy will now serve his apprenticeship in sail, for the *Nesika* is rigged with a staysail that is reported to give her 4½ knots' speed in a good wind. All old salts on the coast staff will now have to take a turn at Port Hardy to qualify in sail if they want to put in their oars around the steam pipes and cracker barrels. Langstroth will now be able to qualify with the Ancient Mariner of the Gulf who knew all the rocks and ledges, for the description we have on file of the *Nesika* has this: 'Owing to the iron keel this ship can be beached or put on the rocks without springing her.' Don't bounce her too high, Charlie."

This buoyant passage from the Newsletter of May 29th., 1937 introduced one of the Forest Service's favourite boats. "We rebuilt her around 1939," Tommy Edwards told me. "We never had much trouble with any boat we rebuilt. We had standards—we never tried to build a corner-post from two pieces, for instance—we made it solid. It paid off. And I used to put kiln-dried decking in. Air-dried decking would always come and go with the weather, so it would leak."

"A good seaworthy boat," Hank Doerksen described the *Nesika*. "I remember having Bill Brash on her once when he came from the interior to take over Echo Bay. Off Lund we had 70-80 m. p. h. winds, and we just laid into them for hours on end. When we stopped off in Pender we found Bill had left his shaving kit by a porthole and it was full of salt water—he was unaccustomed to the coast. The old *Nesika* hadn't had a trip like that in years, either. It shook up all the silt in the fuel tanks, and the next morning we ran out of power and had to change the filters."

She also had the reputation of being a very stiff boat, probably a result of her motorsailer design. "She'd snap upright so hard it would toss you off your feet," said Louie Lorentsen. "Safe but uncomfortable."

As you have heard, Louie Lorentsen was also involved with the *Forest Ranger*, tall and narrow, built for the Forest Service in 1937 by the Victoria Boat Repair Works Ltd. to a design by Tom Halliday 'in co-operation with B. C. Forest Service officers and has incorporated a great many ideas gained from questionnaires sent out to over fifty members of the office and field staff.' (Newsletter)

"You'd get the cheapest job."

Like most committee designs, she was an unsuccessful mish-mash of compromises.

"We came up from Vancouver once in her, in a heavy blow," said Louie. "A north-wester, at night. With her narrow construction you didn't have to put too much weight on the top side before she'd lay flat on her side. We'd bury the nose and the wheelhouse, and the waves would pour past and fill the dinghy, aft on the starboard side. The next sea you climbed up, the weight of the dinghy would heel her right over, and she'd go down the slope sideways. Water was coming down the funnel and pouring over the generator. There were sparks and flames flying all over. Bunny had to stay down there with the fire extinguisher to make sure nothing took hold."

Tommy Edwards summed her up. "She leaked around the cabin and there were no pans in the windows, so the water used to pour in. We had to recanvas the decks. In the hungry Thirties you'd pick the cheapest bid, and you'd get the cheapest job. The *Forest Ranger* only lasted nine years—we sold her around 1946."

The *Tamarack* was a different fish. Once the B. C. Packer number 42, she had been built by Charlie Leslie in 1927, to a sound design. Later Bill Vivian bought her, installed one of his diesels and used her as a private yacht under the name *Miss Vivian*.

The Forest Service bought her in 1938, used her on the West Coast for a year, then rebuilt her. When the *Yellow Cedar* arrived on the scene, they switched her to Echo Bay and Port Hardy. She was a popular boat.

"She was the kind of boat you could go anywhere in, anytime," said Louie Lorentsen. "We took a fair amount of dirty weather in her, travelling to and fro across the bottom of Queen Charlotte Sound. We got into one blow of over 70 knot winds and she handled it all right, although we had to shelter for a little while behind some islands. The *Tamarack* came out of it with salt grass hanging up in the mast top, but she did well."

Arnold Ginnever put it succinctly.

"The *Tamarack*? I ran her for a while. She was a helluva fine boat. She was an old seiner—built like a brick shithouse."

I saw the *Tamarack* recently at Shoal Bay in Sidney. She'd been transferred to the Attorney-General's department in 1976 and they'd taken care of her; she was looking good. They used her for rehabilitation purposes and she bore the appropriate name of *Freedom Found*.

The *Wells Gray* was built in 1927 for Mr. Kidd, the President of the B. C. Electric Railway. Andy Linton and Co. built her to a Halliday design, and she was christened *Hermit*. She was a fine-looking forty-eight footer with a beam of eleven feet six inches. In due course Kidd had *Meander* built, and *Hermit* was put up for sale. The Forest Service bought her in 1938 and named her *Wells Gray* after the Minister of Forests of the time, Mr. Arthur Wellesley Gray.

"I can remember her coming into Thurston Bay from Alert Bay," Tommy Edwards said. "Initially she had a 3-cylinder Gardner with no reverse gearing. You'd stop her, turn a wheel and give her the air, and she'd start backwards. But you had to watch her. Sometimes you'd stop her and she'd stick on top dead centre, and you couldn't restart her either way. So you'd have to run below and bar her over an inch.

"When we first got her she was a bit tender, so we put a weighted keel on her; some of the men were frightened of her. Then in 1948 we rebuilt her at the Maintenance Depot and put a 110 h. p. Gray in her."

Another addition during the rebuilding was a capacious after cabin and a new wheelhouse. *Wells Gray* spent most of her life in the Vancouver Forest District working out of Pender Harbour, and in 1979 the Forest Service decided that her usefulness was at an end.

This was where Paul Stenner came on the scene.

There has always been a ready market for surplus wooden Forest Service boats. This market has become brisker in recent years, partly because of the historic character of the craft, and partly because it is well known that they have received the best of care during their lifetime. Nevertheless the buyers of such a boat know they are letting themselves in for a lot of work, and I'd often wondered what kind of people they are.

Paul Stenner is a pilot with Air Canada and he keeps the *Wells Gray* at Canoe Cove Marina, Sidney, where he welcomed me on board and showed me around the boat. She was in excellent condition and the various modifications which Paul had made blended in with her appearance perfectly. Later as we sat in her cabin drinking coffee and sherry, I asked him how he came to buy her. "I saw her advertised in *Pacific Yachting* in August of 1979, and I remembered the name *Wells Gray*," he said. "So I went over to the Forest Service Maintenance Depot to see her."

"The main thing that impressed me was the space aboard. She had a terrific galley and after cabin, and the only problem was the headroom in the wheelhouse." This was six foot two and Paul stands six foot five, but it didn't deter him. "She had a brand new engine in her, and this was a great selling feature," and so Paul put in a bid.

"It was a time of great excitement waiting for the Purchasing Commission to decide who was the highest bidder. The bids closed at ten in the morning, so I phoned in the afternoon and asked if I'd got the boat."

The Purchasing Commission was astonished at his question. "It'll take two weeks to figure that out, at least," he was informed. "It's a very complicated procedure."

"There's no way it can take that long," Paul told them, and offered a brief solution to their dilemma. "You stack the bids up and work through them, and you put aside a high one. Then if you get a higher one, well, you just put it on top."

This simplistic approach cut no ice with the Purchasing Commission, however, and it was in fact two weeks before Paul learned that he was the new owner of the *Wells Gray.*

"I solved the headroom problem by lowering the deck of the wheelhouse into the engine room," he told me. "I caulked a few seams and pulled the propeller shaft to correct a warp, and that was all I had to do. She's never let me down once. I generally go up the coast in the summers and fish a little, and I found at first that other boats tended to give me a wide berth. Seeing this grey and white official-looking boat, everybody thought I was some kind of Fisheries patrol—particularly when they saw the big Skookum dinghy I was towing. The charter boats *Sealion* and *Marabelle* both have similar dinghies, and people thought I'd caught one of them and impounded it.

"I use her year round, particularly in the winter when I can find a quiet spot around the Gulf Islands or in the States. She's a very comfortable boat; she has an oil stove, and hot water heat up forward. There's something very special about winter cruising, when it's cold and raining outside, and you're warm and comfortable below decks. People show a great deal of appreciation for the *Wells Gray* wherever I go. They stop and look at her when I'm tied up at a dock, and I'm always happy to have them aboard. I'm very proud of her."

So that's the kind of person that buys the surplus Forest Service boats. A man who is prepared to spend a disproportionate amount of time and money in upkeep—for old wooden boats are demanding creatures—in return for comfort and seakindliness, and the style and beauty of a bygone era.

* * * * * *

"I'm very proud of her." Paul Stenner aboard Wells Gray.

We have spoken earlier of the *Dogwood*, the sluggish ex-fishboat which Charlie Yingling used at Lund. Bought by the Ministry in 1939 she was not one of their most successful boats.

"She went to the West Coast in the summer of her first year with us," Tommy Edwards said. "When she came back that fall, she was leaking like a sieve. In that short time there was quite a bit of rot in her. We rebuilt her and sent her up to Port Neville. Eventually she came down to Lund—and it was there that she got into trouble. Vince Hernandez sank her."

If there ever was a Forest Service legend more famous than the Deed of Oliver Clark, it is When Vince Hernandez Sank the *Dogwood*. I'd heard several versions, each accompanied by the cautious words, "But don't quote me on that." Even Hank Doerksen, normally the most frank of men, said that I'd better talk to Vince about it.

So I did. I stayed at the Beach Gardens Resort near Powell River one wild and wet night in October, got in a supply of liquor, and phoned Vince Hernandez. He came quite willingly. It had all happened a long time ago, now.

"Wilf Archer was the assistant Ranger in charge of the *Dogwood*; we were all bachelors at Lund and we all lived on the boats. Then Wilf was transferred, and I inherited the *Dogwood*," he told me.

"I really fell in love with that boat. I thought it was the greatest thing in the world—actually being paid to run a beautiful boat like that. She was a little over thirty-six foot long, with a ten-foot beam, and she had a forward berth and two stern berths. She was a little slow but she handled nicely, and I had no problems with the leaking; by that time they'd fixed her up. I had some good trips with her, and I liked her a lot; she was solid and seaworthy."

Hesitantly, I asked him, "So what went wrong?"

He sighed. "In the summer of 1958 I was taking some scalers around Toba Inlet; I was sleeping in the forward cabin and they slept aft. We were going to work right through one weekend and I decided to fuel up at Cortes Island—because I knew there was a dance there on Saturday night.

"I'd been an assistant Ranger at Whaletown and I knew all the people there, and the dance went on all night. The next day was a beautiful calm summer Sunday, so we decided the scalers would sleep in their bunks while I took them up to Ramsay Arm, then I would tie the boat up and sleep while they were doing their scaling.

"I remember it began to get pretty warm in the cabin as the sun came over the hill, so I opened the windows. I paced back and forth. I sang, and I thought I could handle it. I sat down and propped my eyelids open with my fingertips."

The *Arrawac II*, a charter boat, was heading south at the time with several passengers. One of them decided that the trim form of the *Dogwood*, surging along in the morning sun, would make a good subject for his movie camera. He pointed the camera and pressed the trigger while the *Dogwood* passed between the Rendezvous Islands—a little off her intended course—then made a slow sweep around to port and drove onto a rocky outcrop at full speed.

"That woke me up quite quickly," said Vince. "I ran out of the wheelhouse and looked over the side, hoping that no harm had been done and that I could back off and motor on as though nothing had happened. But the boat began to lurch as it hung up there, and the scalers came running out on deck in their underpants. The boat began to go down. The scalers seemed to blame me for it

"It was high tide and the Dogwood *had stopped sinking."*

all, and one of them said he had a fair bit of money in his pockets but he wasn't going back into the cabin to fetch it, not with the boat sinking. So I went into the aftercabin and grabbed his trousers.

"Meanwhile the *Arrawac II* was filming the whole drama and the scalers were getting even angrier because they felt it was a breach of privacy, with them being in their underpants. This aspect didn't concern me too much. I just felt sick."

It was high tide and the *Dogwood* had stopped sinking, so the *Arrawac II* pulled her off and they beached her in a nearby bay. Now Vince had to face the repercussions. They called the *B. C. Forester* which happened to be in the area, and were taken back to Lund. Vince told his Ranger, Jim Winslow. Jim called the District Forester, who said he would meet them back at the wreck. The District Forester flew in, stone-faced, and almost the first words he said to Vince were:

"I suppose you know you're no longer working for the Forest Service."

"I'd suspected that much," said Vince unhappily.

Tommy Edwards told me the end of the *Dogwood's* story. "Bob Swan went up with Bouch and the *Syrene*, and some of the boys from the plant. They got the water out of her at low water and pumped cement into the bows. Then they towed her down to the Depot, and we fixed her up and sold her."

Vince's story has a happier ending. "Later the Forest Service let it be known that if I wanted to make another application for a job it would be received sympathetically. So after a short spell with Crown Zellerbach I rejoined. I got a job at Thurston Bay as launch engineer on the *Forest Ranger*, believe it or not!"

*   *   *   *   *   *

An unusual vessel was the *White Cloud*.

She was built by Ah King of Hong Kong in 1911, sixty feet long, a motor-sailer with a definite look of the oriental about her. During the Thirties she arrived in B. C. where she was used to haul gunpowder to mining and logging camps up and down the coast. The Forest Service bought her in 1941 and re-built her.

She had a pronounced sheer at the bows, exaggerated by stepped monkey-rails, and it was this more than anything, perhaps, which gave her the rakish Oriental look. Tommy lowered all this and smoothed it out into lines more acceptable to western eyes. She had an old Swedish engineer at this time, and when he saw the result he said, regretfully,

"Gee whiz, Tom, you took that hungry look off her."

The small hut of a wheelhouse was removed from its aft position too; replaced by a larger centrally-placed structure of recognizably Forest Service design. Her sea trial was an exciting occasion, according to the Newsletter of July, 1947.

"As the ship's clock showed exactly 12.51 p. m., (Jim McDonald hurriedly translated this into 'bells and tinkles') the *Cloud*, gleaming in the sun and with the sure hands of Tommy Edwards at the wheel, slowly warped her 60-foot length from the wharf and nosed out into the channel.

"One of the first features that came to everyone's notice as the *Cloud* picked up speed was that there was absolutely no vibration either in the wheelhouse or below decks. This condition held throughout the entire test run and must certainly be a tribute to her construction.

"... the rakish Oriental look." White Cloud *before her conversion.*

"As the *Cloud* rounded Point Grey and neared the start of the measured mile, we noticed that we were not alone, as we could see the *Maple*, formerly *Tahuna III*, coming into line about a mile off the stern, obviously intending to make the mile run as well. This injected a certain amount of extra excitement into those aboard the *Cloud*, as they all envisioned a real honest-to-goodness race."

Then came the real excitement.

"After running almost the complete mile with no signs of any kinks or bugs coming to the fore, the *Cloud* suddenly began to veer madly to port. Tommy Edwards, exerting every bit of his strength, could not make her answer to the wheel. She just refused to budge one inch to starboard! After a few nerve-wracking moments, during which both Edwards and Farmer struggled with the tiller, they threw the diesel into neutral and the *Cloud*, losing way fast and rolling slightly on her own wash, came around in a wide arc and stopped. By this time the *Maple* had overhauled us and was standing about twenty feet off the starboard side waiting to see if she could be of any help.

"The first thing that came to everyone's mind was that there must be something jammed in the rudder or that the steering chains were caught up on something . . . "

Curiously though, on a second attempt at the measured mile everything was in order.

"On the run back the discussion of what could have caused this mad quirk went on unabated. The consensus of opinion seemed to be that after all this was what test runs were for, that is, to shake out the 'wrinkles' which just about every boat in the world possesses at one point in her career. The *Cloud's* specific trouble was solved a few days later, when Tommy Edwards and Dick Farmer had two-thirds of the rudder balance removed and also reduced the area of the rudder itself. This resulted in an increase of speed and improved performance all around."

Thirty-five years later I sat in Tommy Edwards' living room.

"What really happened, Tommy?" I asked.

He laughed. "She was touching bottom, that's all. Just hanging up in the sand a little; it dragged the rudder to one side. So we moved into deeper water and she responded just fine."

"But why all the mystery?"

"Just to add a little colour to the article, I guess. And I'll tell you something else. At the time of the rebuild she needed new fuel tanks, and money wasn't too plentiful. I told Jim McDonald and he said, 'Can't afford it, Tom'.

" 'Well, ' I said, 'they're in pretty grim shape.'

" 'I'll get Max to test them,' he said.

"I said, 'Fine.' And I went to see Max. And Max said, 'We really need those new tanks, don't we, Tom?' And I said, 'We sure do.'

"So Max put the water pressure on them—to test them, he said. He sealed them up and used the full water main pressure—around 225 pounds. Of course, they split all to hell. So we got our new tanks."

He grinned at me comfortably, retired from the Forest Service. "Now it can be told," he said.

The *White Cloud* didn't last long after that. One day in 1949 Jim McDonald was on his way from Ocean Falls to Bella Coola to take an inventory of Forest Service equipment. In Dean Channel a fire broke out aboard the *White Cloud* caused, it was later surmised, by a leak from the auxiliary. Jim McDonald, Ollie Antella and Neil McMillan the engineer took to a skiff and, pulling away, watched the *White Cloud* burn to the waterline, taking the inventory books with her.

Another vessel operating in nearby waters around that time was the *White Spruce*, a bridge-deck cruiser built in 1932 as the *Sea Belle III*. She was forty-three feet long with a beam of ten feet and a Hercules Russel 120 h. p. engine. The Forest Service bought her in 1945.

"We found quite a bit of rot in her," said Tommy ruefully.

She spent her days at Ocean Falls until she was replaced in 1962 by the *Balsam*, when she was sold.

And finally from that era there was the *Maple*, thirty-seven feet of solid worth, built in 1945 by J. T. Taylor of Vancouver as a motor-sailer and bought by the Forest Service in 1947, at which time she bore the name of *Tahuna III*.

"She was a dandy boat," Louie Lorentsen told me. "One of the most solidly-built boats we had. If she had a fault, she was wet. She'd scoop water over the bow quite easily — but I've had her in heavy seas and she rode just like a duck."

Generally she was used as a swing boat, a temporary replacement for boats undergoing refit. Most of the coastal Rangers sailed on her at one time or another.

"She was a very wet boat," said Frank Tannock. "One trip I took the *Nesika* up to Port Hardy and brought the *Maple* back. It was winter and there was a heck of a blow on. We sat for a couple of days in Port Hardy waiting for the weather to calm down and the engineer was nattering about wasting the holidays he was due for. Finally I told him that tomorrow we'd take a run out to Round Island and see what the weather was like in Johnstone Strait.

"So the next day we went out and turned into the storm — it was still howling — and after three minutes of it I said to the engineer, 'We can't buck this. We're going back.'

"'You're going to try to turn around, in this?'

"'That's what I'm going to do,' I said.

"'We'll never make it,' he squawked.

"'You just hang on,' I said.

"So I waited until I could see a long swell coming, went over the top and made the turn. Now the *Maple* was pretty slow on the turn, and just before we got our stern to the weather we were quartering, and the next wave hit us. My God. It nearly sent us to the bottom. All the stuff came off the shelves and she was drenched inside and out. But she came up and shivered like a dog, then off we went again. She was a good ship, the *Maple*."

Arnold Ginnever said, "I liked the *Maple*. A lot of guys thought she was half submarine—but she was really built. The only thing I didn't like was the engine compartment immediately under the wheelhouse floor. You had to stand right on top of that screaming Jimmy. But she was tight; you could take a green one against the wheelhouse window and not a drop would come inside."

In 1979 the *Maple* was sold to David Martin-Smith of Victoria. She's berthed at Westport Marina in Sidney, and I see the solid lines of her from the Pat Bay Highway, every evening on my way home.

* * * * * *

And then there was the *Balsam*, bought in 1949, forty-two feet with a twelve foot beam, built in 1934.

"When we got the *Balsam* with its big flared bow, we used to think we'd got the world by the tail," said Don Owen. "We could head into the wind and the *Balsam* would just split the waves and throw them back. But she'd yaw all over the place in a following sea. It was that big square stern on her."

Tommy Edwards said knowledgeably: "The trouble with her bow was that the flare came past the break of the deck. It stuck out, and rubbed against piles. That's a bad fault on a boat."

"But she was a beautiful launch," Don insisted. "I was as proud as punch when I got her. She had an automatic pilot—the only one in the Forest Service." He grinned. "I remember once we were going into Jervis Inlet on a beautiful calm day. Denny Allison was motoring a little astern in the *Cherry II*, to our starboard. Between us we were going to visit all the loggers in the inlet.

"We set the automatic pilot. It seemed simple enough. Then we sat in the sun on the pilothouse roof, my engineer and I, having a cup of coffee. Denny in the *Cherry* had lashed his wheel ahead, and he was dozing on his pilothouse roof.

"All of a sudden the *Balsam* decided to take a big sweep to starboard." His

". . . we used to think we'd got the world by the tail."

eyes widened as he relived the horror of the moment. "Jesus Christ. The engineer and I scrambled down into the wheelhouse and fought over the automatic pilot, trying to disengage it. The *Balsam* headed straight for the *Cherry*. Neither of us had the presence of mind to yell to Denny, asleep on his roof. We got the *Balsam* under control in the nick of time, and veered away.

"But we were so close to sending two Forest Service boats to the bottom, and ruining our careers. We never used the automatic pilot after that."

Don was stationed at Pender Harbour at the time. It was a little later that *Cherry II* and *Balsam* finally came to blows, with a new assistant Ranger in charge of the Blimp.

"A randy young bugger," Don described him, "always looking for an excuse to take his launch down to Vancouver. Well, he came to me one day and told me he'd touched bottom and the propeller needed fixing. It didn't sound good to me when he revved it up — although I wouldn't have put it past him to have wrapped a piece of cable around the propeller to prove his point.

"So we set off the next day with the *Cherry II* rafted alongside the *Balsam*. Off Half-Moon Bay we met a lot of slop. Suddenly the *Cherry* smashed

against the side of the *Balsam* and lifted the side decking away from the *Balsam's* hull. Hell of a crash. So we put the *Cherry* on the end of a tow rope and reached the Maintenance Depot five hours later. We got a ride down town and the assistant Ranger got his night out.

"The next morning Jim McDonald took me aside in a fatherly way. 'Gee, Don' he said, 'if I didn't know you better I'd say this was a put-up job. There's not a goddamned thing wrong with the *Cherry II*. I think you've been conned. But the damage to the *Balsam*—that's going to take ten days to repair.'

"The way it ended up," he said sadly, "was that I got a real sizzler of a reprimand from the District Forester for damaging my boat, and my assistant got a weekend in Vancouver!"

*   *   *   *   *   *

The *Forest Ranger, Nesika, Wells Gray, Tamarack, Dogwood, White Cloud, White Spruce, Maple* and *Balsam*. These stout wooden vessels formed the nucleus of John Paynter's navy in the early days of his command. Well-built and well-maintained, most of them are still afloat and, after their years of service, are continuing their days as pleasure craft around the coast of British Columbia.

But back in 1946 John Paynter was newly arrived, enthusiastic, bringing to his job a wealth of experience and talent. Before long he began to mould the fleet to his own ideas.

THE RANGER LAUNCHES—III

"When I arrived in 1946," John said, "the boats didn't contain much more than an engine and an oil stove, head, sink, compass and radio. They were primitive. But gradually people's expectations rose and we had to start installing hot water systems, auxiliary engines in case we got caught with our batteries flat, better lighting, AM and FM radios, and mechanical anchor winches.

"We had to remember that a lot of work was being done by people who were basically landlubbers, so we had to install things like boom winches for handling tenders, because we didn't dare risk somebody letting go of a crank handle while hoisting a boat out of the water, and knocking his teeth out."

One day John was a passenger in a launch whose Ranger had a somewhat unnerving habit of hugging the shore, slipping over the shallows, weaving past rocks. After half an hour of this John suggested, with due deference:

"Wouldn't it be safer if we kept to the middle of the channel?"

The Ranger gave him a brief, scornful glance. "The middle of the channel? You should always avoid the middle of channels. Didn't you know? That's where the reefs are."

*   *   *   *   *   *

Then there was the Ranger who went to Alert Bay. He'd never been on a boat before, but he was lucky — the station launch had an experienced engineer who started off by showing him around. The Ranger was impressed, particularly by the launch's cooking arrangements.

"Nice kitchen you've got here," he observed.

"Sure is," the engineer agreed. "And if you'd like to step down into the basement I'll show you the engine!"

This, then, was the situation John met when he arrived. Boats were needed for getting around but seamanship was not regarded as a prerequisite for a Ranger — not to the extent that a knowledge of forestry practices was. As Don Owen once said, "Wherever we can replace a boat with a road, we will do it."

But meanwhile the boats were necessary, and John set about augmenting the fleet. In 1949 he bought the *Alpine Fir II*, built in 1947 by Gordon H. Oliver of North Vancouver as the *Letitia II*. Some of Hank Doerksen's adventures with her have already been mentioned. She is forty-six feet long with a beam

"Built in 1947 as the Letitia II.*"*

of eleven foot ten. Originally she was somewhat underpowered, boasting a Buda which could only push her along at 6½ knots or so, but she was later re-engined with a Jimmy which gave her a speed of well over ten knots. She spent most of her time around Thurston Bay and Kelsey Bay, where she is presently stationed. In general Rangers speak of her with affection.

But you can't please everyone. Arnold Ginnever told me:

"Sure, she's beautiful to look at, with the superstructure all finished in varnish. But she isn't a strong boat. I didn't like being out in any kind of weather with her.

"Once we went across Nodales Channel to a handlogger's camp. As we came in, there was a strong south-easter blowing. At the last moment I noticed this goddamned great drag saw on the dock, with the blade sticking out at an angle. I thought to myself: no way am I going to make a landing near that. So I backed off and decided to land ahead of the thing. There was plenty of room.

"But the wind caught the *Alpine Fir* and just skidded her across the water like a blown-up paper bag, and the point of this drag saw gouged all the way

along the varnish. That's the kind of thing that would happen with the *Alpine Fir*. She was lightly built, and the wind could get a hold of you."

Arnold was in the minority. The *Alpine Fir II* has proved a popular boat and, according to Tommy Edwards, was exceptionally well built by Mr. Oliver of hand-picked yellow cedar and mahogany which had been aged for three years.

There is an interesting footnote to her story. On June 3rd., 1973 John Paynter received the following letter:

"Dear Sirs:

In November of 1949, my late husband Gordon Oliver sold to the Forestry Service our motor vessel *Letitia II*, which you renamed '*Alpine Fir*' and is stationed at Kelsey Bay.

I have a request that I hope you will give some consideration to. Due to sentimentality, I would very much like to have the ship's bell that is mounted on the outside of the wheelhouse, which has engraved on it '*Letitia II*'. (It is also one of my names.)

I know this is an unusual request, but I have often wished I had this bell, and as the vessel's name is different anyway now, perhaps it would be possible for you to send it to me. Twenty years is quite a long time to keep a dream, isn't it!

Thank you,
Yours truly,
Mrs. M. L. Warren."

How could John resist such a charming request? The bell was removed and cleaned up, and Wilf Archer sent it to Mrs. Warren.

Three years after the arrival of the *Alpine Fir II*, John Paynter bought her sister-ship, the *Forynt*, also built by Gordon Oliver. Again, she was in beautiful condition and needed very little additional work to equip her for the rigors of Forest Service work. She was renamed the *Western Yew*, and Louie Lorentsen had her for a while at Chatham Channel. Frank Tannock told the story of her delivery there.

"She had a hydraulic clutch which took a while to get into reverse. Louie was at anchor in the *Douglas Fir II* and I had to get alongside him, in quite a blow. I was trying to get headed into the wind, but every time I approached the *Douglas Fir* I came broadside on, the reverse wouldn't take hold in time and I'd skewer the wheelhouse door of Louie's boat with a fairlead. Louie was getting pretty irritated in there. But when he started operating the boat himself he began to appreciate the problem."

Frank Tannock was Louie's supervisor at the time, and tells of a big game hunter whom they picked up at the head of Knight Inlet. The hunter was wealthy and world-renowned, and had just bagged a grizzly of record proportions. He'd done everything and seen everything.

A grey whale broke surface some distance off the starboard bow of the *Western Yew.*

"We'll close in a bit," said Frank. "You'll be able to get a photo."

"I've seen plenty of whales," replied the hunter loftily.

The whale surfaced again, about thirty yards away. It was big.

"By God," said the hunter. "Maybe I will get a shot of her." He leaped to the wheelhouse door, flung it open and levelled his camera at the empty, heaving sea.

The *Western Yew* ploughed on.

"Come on, you bastard!" shouted the hunter.

The whale came rocketing out of the water ten feet away, monumental as it rose into the sky, water cascading from its flanks, barnacle-encrusted, big as a church tower and dappled with moss.

With a squeal of alarm the hunter flung himself backwards. The whale smacked broadside onto the surface of the sea with a sound like a nuclear device. The *Western Yew* was tossed aside. The sea subsided, a welter of foam and whirlpools marking the disappearance of the whale. Shaking, the big game hunter climbed to his feet.

"We were all scared," chuckled Frank, remembering. "We were lucky the whale hadn't fallen across the boat—it would have broken us in two. But that big game hunter; I can still see him lying on his back, eyes popping out of their sockets. He got a hell of a good photograph of the wheelhouse roof!"

*   *   *   *   *   *

By now the Forest Service had begun to build its own boats again, and in 1950 the *Tachi III* had slipped down the ways: a thirty-two footer for lake use at Fort St. James. Now came something bigger; in 1953 the forty-four foot *Forest Ranger II* was completed at the Fraser River Maintenance Depot, patterned after the *Alpine Fir II* and the *Western Yew.*

Considerable discussions took place before her keel was laid.

"Mr. Bassett commenced by expressing the opinion that the launch *Balsam,*

"By now the Forest Service had begun to build its own boats again."

now in service, has been satisfactory in most respects, and he would like to see the new boat modelled closely along the same lines," reported John Paynter in 1951, adding tactfully, "I pointed out that whilst the *Balsam* was admittedly one of our best boats, we in Victoria felt that she does not necessarily represent the ultimate in specialized design. The *Balsam* suffered from being bow heavy as a result of her pilot house and engine being too far forward."

It seems to have been a stormy meeting, because John's report continues, "Mr. Bassett then virtually stipulated that the pilot house *must* be forward to give good visibility despite the fact that it appears desirable to mount the engine beneath the pilot house both for good utilization of space and easy removal of the engine from the boat should that become necessary." There was some agreement, however: "At this point in the proceedings it was also stated by the District officials that a shower is unnecessary and it was agreed by all that one toilet would be adequate."

Discussion continued. John suggested placing the Ranger's office abaft the pilot house with the engine under it. Mr. Bassett did not favour this arrangement. Mr. McDonald said he would like to see funnel exhausts abandoned in favour of a water-cooled installation. Tommy Edwards wanted to see a sturdier hull. John pointed out that all these factors, plus a request from Mr. Bassett for doubled fuel capacity, would result in a very slow boat. It was considered desirable, however, that the new boat should be faster than the *Balsam*.

John summarized: "This meeting has stated its requirements regarding layout, strength and hull form — and I have asked you: will you accept what performance this combination will give us? To which Mr. Bassett has replied, 'Don't give us a lesser performance than that of the *Balsam*'!"

A fairly good example of the problems encountered when designing a boat by committee — reinforced by a reply from Mr. Bassett, who reported that there was a misunderstanding: it was the *Alpine Fir II* that the District was thinking of, not the *Balsam*!

So the boat went ahead on the lines of the *Alpine Fir II*, with a GM 6-71 diesel. This brought about the need for a reversion to the funnel exhausts. Harry Hill recommended:

"The installation of a stack, this to eliminate the wet exhaust, provide an outlet for stove pipe and better ventilation for the engine room...As you cannot depend on porthole ventilators, air becomes quite a problem with GM installations. We have three cases where galley fires have been sucked out in the type of vessel where the engine room is connected to the galley by a doorway, the *Cherry II* being one of them."

With so many problems and so many differing requirements, it is surprising to report that the *Forest Ranger II*, when it eventually took to the water, became a successful and popular boat.

Possibly as a reaction to this many-minded design and its attendant frustrations, possibly because he had settled in and felt he had something to offer, John determined that the next Ranger launch built by the Forest Service should be his kind of boat.

He had already paved the way with three smaller craft; fast planing launches intended to be the successor to the Blimps, and to herald a new era on the coast. The *Forest Supervisor* was built in 1955, the *Pacific Yew* and the *Yellow Pine* in 1956. The *Forest Supervisor* was thirty feet and the other two were twins of thirty-three feet. Their reception was mixed. Said Hank Doerksen of the *Supervisor*:

"The idea was to give Ranger Supervisors fast transportation up and down the coast. But instead of putting twin marine Perkins in the *Forest Supervisor* they got a good buy on a couple of land diesels and converted them for salt-water cooling. They were real pigs. The boat developed a terrible reputation and was eventually relegated to Ganges. I had an old Ranger who'd been used to the Blimps—boats with some weight to them, a good hull and a good wheel. He was getting on in years and he wasn't too adaptable—and here he was faced with this monstrosity bobbing like a cork on top of the water, with two sets of controls! Well, coming in to land he always tried to handle it like a Blimp. He'd hit one throttle and then the other, and Christ, the first thing you knew he'd be spinning in a circle. He never did get the hang of that boat. And the engines were always breaking down—and quite often they'd have to send to England for a part.

"Tommy Edwards will probably defend that boat, but with a great deal of difficulty."

So of course the next time I saw Tommy I asked him. "They never used her enough," he said sourly. "And they didn't look after her properly. I remember we had her into the Maintenance Depot once, and the propellers were so encrusted with barnacles they looked like coral reefs."

One stormy day the *Henry Foss*, an American tug, was heading north to pick up a tow of logs. In a fierce south-east gale she sought shelter between Prevost and Saltspring Islands. At about two o'clock in the morning she struck a reef off Ganges harbour. The skipper threw her big Enterprise engine into reverse, and as she drove astern the reef dragged the bottom off her. She sank very quickly. The crew had piled into the workboat but as the ship went down she heeled, and the mast capsized the boat.

The morning ferry found a survivor clinging to the upturned lifeboat.

"We got a call at Ganges Ranger station," said Hank Doerksen. "It happened I was the only one there, so I picked up a local man and we managed to get the *Forest Supervisor* going. It was still blowing a hell of a gale. We headed into it, bouncing all over the place. And in the end we picked up two bodies. Hypothermia. I'd have sworn they were still alive as we closed on them, floating face up in their jackets with their eyes open."

*   *   *   *   *   *

With the advantage of hindsight, John Paynter now says, "I tried to introduce the concept of the high-speed planing boats too soon. I was young and speed was attractive to me, and I thought my experience with Vospers could be useful to the Forest Service. But Rangers look on their boats as something more than transportation; they're a place to live and an office. High-speed craft had to be somewhat smaller, and this resulted in cramped quarters for the men."

In 1958 John had yet to learn this lesson, and he introduced the *Western Hemlock*.

Forty feet overall, she had an eleven foot beam and a planing hull double planked with yellow cedar inside and Honduras mahogany out. She displaced 21,500 lbs loaded, and was powered by two G. M. 6/71 diesels. Her maximum speed was twenty-four m. p. h. and she cruised at twenty m. p. h. She looked like a motor torpedo boat. She was intended for the Prince Rupert region and her first, fast run north has already been described.

On December 15th., the District presented its critique:

"The *Western Hemlock* is more spacious, comfortable and better equipped than the smaller *Yellow Pine*, but it is not a suitable answer to Ranger requirements of this District. There is no hold. The boat is not designed for working purposes and must suffer whenever used for such duties as fire fighting. This is considered the most serious fault of all and one which all Ranger boats should overcome. Not suited to Nass River, Skeena River and Esctall Rivers, and similar waters open to ordinary boats of this tonnage, due to unprotected propellors and design. Not suited to outside waters because of design. A very wet boat when used at half speed in rough seas."

Despite all this, the report ends on a note of optimism. "The boat is a very fine craft and suitable for supervisory work and similar duties in areas where floats and dockage is the rule and not the exception, as is the case in the Prince Rupert District.

"We shall, however, take great pride and pleasure in the use of the *Western Hemlock* to its utmost capabilities. However, a displacement type of launch, such as the *Lillian D*, appears to be the logical solution to our requirements."

John told me, "One thing I've learned over all these years is to give the launch operators what they want. If you don't you can be sure that sooner or later they'll have an accident to prove you wrong, one way or another."

The *Western Hemlock's* first accident occurred the following year. She collided with an R. C. M. P. boat moored in Prince Rupert harbour.

"In 1958 John . . . introduced the Western Hemlock.*"*

The Ranger, impatient to get away from the dock, cast off the lines and jumped aboard. His engineer had not yet appeared from below to take the controls, so the Ranger himself backed the boat towards the R. C. M. P. craft. However, in his excitement he then pushed the throttle levers instead of the clutches. The engineer, emerging quickly from below, threw the clutches; but by then it was too late. The *Western Hemlock* crashed into the R. C. M. P. boat, puncturing two planks.

The main problem with the fast planing launches was deadheads, however. The boats' speed reduces the time the crew have to react; moreover, the attitude of the planing boat tends to take it over the deadhead instead of pushing it aside, and propellers get damaged.

Russ Campbell described such an incident. By this time the *Western Hemlock* had been transferred south.

"I hit a deadhead. It bent one of the shafts and the propeller came round and chewed a hole in the stern. We began to take on water fast and had to put her up on the beach. We found some ply and smeared it with butter, screwed it over the hole and took her to Vancouver on one engine. Tommy Edwards was a bit shocked when he saw our patch!"

In 1960 the *Forest Dispatcher* was built: a fast planing sister-ship to the *Western Hemlock*. This time they did not make the mistake of sending such a boat to the rough waters of Prince Rupert; the *Forest Dispatcher* was based at Lund. And by now the Forest Service had realized the benefits of public relations — the launching received press coverage.

"A sleek newcomer will take her place amongst the small power craft of the lower coastal waters this evening (22 June; 7.00 p. m.) when the 40-foot B. C. Forest Service Ranger launch slides down the ways . . . designed to improve forest protection and general management services in the Vancouver Forest District . . . in charge of Ranger Harley Norbirg.

The new boat will be christened by Mrs. R. C. Swan, wife of the Engine Foreman at the Marine Station who is scheduled to receive his 25-year service pin during the launching ceremonies.

Under construction for the past year, *Forest Dispatcher* displaces 12 tons, has an 11 foot beam, complete accommodation for three, and is powered by a matched pair of 4-cylinder General Motors turbo diesels capable of developing 380 horsepower. She is expected to cruise at 16 mph and her estimated maximum speed is 20 mph. *Dispatcher's* cruising range is 200 miles . . . "

She was therefore a little slower than the *Western Hemlock*. By 1976 this had become a sore point with her operator, by then Ranger Vic Doerksen, who requested that the Maintenance Depot:

" . . . repower the launch *Forest Dispatcher* to restore her original performance and if possible make it equal to that of her sister vessel the *Western Hemlock* . . . The request for speed in the 16-17 knot range becomes increasingly valid in view of the restrictions on overtime . . . the present 12 knot speed means that the launch is operating very inefficiently in a semi-planing condition."

John Paynter said, "We repowered her with two six-cylinder diesels, and they made all the difference. Ten years after they were built, those two boats had become the most popular vessels in the Vancouver Region. By that time the Union was gathering strength and a new generation of Rangers was at the helm. They didn't want to spend their weeks chugging around the coast. They wanted to get to the job, do it, and get home."

*   *   *   *   *   *

John's next acquisition was a forty-eight foot displacement launch which had originally been built for the use of the Provincial Police in the Queen Charlottes by W. R. Menschen of Vancouver, in 1948, as P. M. L. 17. By 1963 she was in the possession of the Provincial Fish and Wildlife under the Branch name of *Otter*. As she was surplus to their requirements they offered her to the Forest Service. John named her the *Poplar III* and sent her to the Prince Rupert District where she proved very successful.

"We repowered her in 1972," said Tommy Edwards, "but we never changed her, except to put some ballast in to compensate for the lighter engine."

In 1963 L. W. Lehrle, the District Forester at Prince Rupert wrote: "Since the *Poplar III* arrived she has been used by the Prince Rupert Ranger staff and they are more than pleased with the vessel . . . You are aware of our local conditions and the fact that a high-speed launch of the *Western Hemlock* type is not suited to these waters. We would much prefer to replace the *Western Hemlock* with the *Poplar III* and continue to use the *Lillian D*, even if the use (of the latter) must be restricted by sea conditions until the new craft is available . . . "

A thin file is a sign of a successful boat. The only sour note in *Poplar III's* record appears in 1968, when W. F. Tuttle, the Assistant District Forester, made comment on a familiar peril of the sea:

> "When the *Poplar III* is in for refit this month, could you please arrange to see what can be done to permit starting the auxiliary motor with more safety to personnel. There have been recurring accidents where the starting handle disengages and flies up to catch the employee on the head producing cuts and swellings and teeth knocked loose. Is there any possibility of relocating the auxiliary motor to allow more room for evasive action?"

The *Poplar III* is still at Prince Rupert, still performing sterling service. By 1965 the question of the *Lillian D's* retirement became a matter of urgen-

"A real nice boat."

cy and John started looking for a replacement. He found another forty-eight footer of similar design to the *Poplar III* but more lightly constructed, again working for the Fish and Wildlife Branch, named the *Otter II*. She had been built in 1959 at Star Shipyard of yellow cedar planking, gumwood sheathed at bow and waterline. She was equipped with radar, radio and echo sounder for navigation in the frequently fog-shrouded Dean Channel. Although it was originally intended that she operate out of Ocean Falls—for which reason she was named the *Dean Ranger*—she has in fact spent most of her working life at Kitimat.

"A real nice boat," Ron Hawkins told me. "We never had any trouble with her."

* * * * * *

The *Leola Vivian* was built in 1939 at Sidney for Bill Vivian of diesel engine fame. She was fifty-five foot eight in length, fourteen foot three beam, of

yellow cedar throughout. In due course she passed into the care of the Department of Lands, who named her the *B. C. Surveyor*. In 1966 she was transferred to the Forest Service.

On March 22nd., 1967, John Paynter wrote to Miss Lorna Clark of Hamilton, Ontario, as follows:

"Dear Miss Clark,

I am writing in my capacity as the Honorary Curator of the B.C. Forest Service Museum, to explain why we are sending you at this time the enclosed colour print of the citation to your late uncle, Oliver Clark.

As you will see from the enclosed photograph, a Forest Service vessel was named after your uncle by Miss Patullo representing the then Premier of the Province. This vessel was retired after 36 years service on the coast and is now to be replaced by another vessel named the *Oliver Clark II*, in order to perpetuate the memory of one who has rightfully taken his place as the folk-hero of the Forest Service..."

The *Oliver Clark II* is an interesting vessel in other ways. She was built for demonstration purposes and so had a big Vivian engine together with large capacity fuel tanks for a projected voyage to Australia. In order to accommodate all this—the engine weighed eight tons—the boat had to built in sections, and the frames on one side were put in after the engine and tanks were installed. She was later rebuilt at the Marine Depot, and the engine was donated to the Maritime Museum in Vancouver.

One day in 1981 I went to Bella Coola with John Paynter to see her. Since the aircraft used on the Bella Coola run had recently crashed into a mountain with the loss of all aboard, I suggested that we go by car. I had never driven the road from Williams Lake to Bella Coola before but it seemed, at the time, a safe enough procedure. Of course, I had to reckon with John's driving which consists of a series of narrowly-averted disasters. His style is to set the car on its course and then remove both hands from the wheel in frenzied gesticulation as he illustrates some point, seizing the wheel as the car runs on the shoulder, jerking it on course again, then once more removing his hands. So I arranged it so that I would take the wheel through the mountains.

The descent into the Bella Coola valley was unforgettable; a gravel road crudely hacked into the mountainside like a notch cut by the axe of some immense and drunken logger, constantly reversing course as it switchbacked down, frequently disappearing around blind corners wide enough for one car, the surface seemingly composed of buttered ball-bearings so that the slightest touch on the brakes sent the car skittering to the edge of a thousand-foot drop . . . I forgot to mention that I have been terrified of heights since I was a child. Every so often my senses would reel and I would be gripped by an almost overwhelming temptation to drive quickly over the edge and put an end to the whole horrible business. It would only require a touch on the wheel and it was so much cleaner, that way.

And after all that, *Oliver Clark II* was not at the dock. Only the little fibre-glass *Forest Scout* was there, bouncing like a baby in the lap of the sea. The mountains closed in around us and *Oliver Clark II* was somewhere on the high seas, and wouldn't be back for days, so we were told. As we stood there glumly, staring down the inlet, John told me an interesting story.

"Back in the early Seventies we were going to put in a new float here, and we decided that the most effective anchors would be clusters of old railways wheels threaded on chains. You can see some of them now, just below the surface. They weigh about 700 lbs each.

"So we bought 200 of them and shipped them up by Northland Navigation. When these wheels were unloaded at the wharf the dockside loungers lifted their eyebrows and hurried off in the direction of the beer parlour.

"Later we heard that an overnight property boom had been sparked by the rumour that the Pacific Great Eastern Railway was going to construct a spur line up the valley, and was already shipping in equipment. The boom collapsed the next day, however, when more knowledgeable people inspected the wheels and took note of their age and condition."

So the next day we headed back with the mountain looming before me, and John suggesting that everything would be fine if he drove and I huddled on the floor at the back, so that he would have nobody to gesticulate at; with a blanket over me so I wouldn't be able to see out. I had a better idea in the form of a bottle of Johnny Walker Red Label at which, half way along the valley, I took a deep and satisfying drag. Emboldened, I pointed the car at the mountain.

Shortly after the first hairpin bend, however, I had degenerated into a quivering blob of protoplasm, cold sober and frozen to the wheel as though in rigor mortis. I managed to get my foot on the brake and shortly afterwards, tumbled out of the car onto firm ground. "I'll walk," I said to John.

And so I trotted to the top while John drove behind, stopping every mile or so to admire the view. And in all that eight kilometres I saw no other traffic. Nothing; not even a mountain goat. Down at the District Office they had laughed at my predicament, and told me that buses used that road, and semi-trailers; but I don't believe them. I believe Bella Coola is a dream place like Brigadoon, which springs into existence fully-grown when someone with a clean mind and a stout heart—like myself—drives down that mountain; and the rest of the time is just an empty valley, timeless and tranquil.

John, however, is a practising sceptic. "I see fishing charters out of Bella Coola advertised in the magazines, which proves the place exists. What's more, I'm always a bit suspicious of these charters. I keep thinking they might be using the *Oliver Clark II*," he said darkly.

*　*　*　*　*　*

In 1966 the Marine Depot built their biggest wooden vessel so far; a displacement launch of forty-eight foot four with a thirteen foot two beam. The original intention was to name her the *Golden Spruce* but it was found that this name was already taken, so the new boat was christened the *Coast Ranger* at a small ceremony on November 9th.

"We liked the design of the *Poplar III*," said Tommy Edwards, "so we went to the same architect to have the *Coast Ranger* designed. The hull was changed a little and we put the wheelhouse higher. To compensate for this we put a weighted keel on her, but we soon got complaints that she rolled a lot. I'm sure that part of this is imaginary, because the higher wheelhouse swings through a wider arc. We sent her up to Prince Rupert for a while but they sent her back; they didn't want her."

He went on, "In the old days nobody bothered about rolling—hell, on the old *Lillian D* you could walk up the doors. But nowadays people get worried about it, even though the *Coast Ranger* passed her stability test. She's a fast roller, and a fast-rolling boat will outlast the crew. It's the sluggish ones the sea will come aboard and kill."

Other people speak well of the *Coast Ranger*, which has operated out of Port McNeill for some years. Her accommodation is good and her construction is excellent, with yellow cedar planking which the Forest Service had some difficulty in obtaining. She was the last of the wooden boat era, and John Paynter admitted that she was something of an anachronism in other ways; in selecting her displacement design he was reacting to the lack of acceptance of the fast planing *Western Hemlock* and *Forest Dispatcher*.

In 1980 a very successful modification was made to the *Coast Ranger* which

"She was the last of the wooden boat era."

has silenced her more nervous operators. John Paynter tells how it came about.

"Bordie Grant's son had a fishing boat, and he had a problem running with his pole stabilizers out when he was motoring through the fishing grounds at night. There was always the fear that they would foul somebody's nets, or even a log. So he fitted stabilizers which stick out horizontally from the keel, attached to vertical plates dropping from the side of the hull. We scaled them up to eight feet long for the *Coast Ranger* and although they don't look too seamanlike they make all the difference to her stability.

"Funnily enough, when we were fitting them we had a Spanish seasonal skipper who was taking the *Forest Ranger II* up to Rupert, and he'd seen the identical design fitted to the Spanish fishing fleet as long ago as World War II. They make the vessel as stiff as a church."

In the early years of the century there were very few roads through the forested areas of the province, so people travelled mostly by river. The original river boats used by trappers and prospectors were usually hand whipsawn out of the nearest available tree. When the Forest Service came into being the Rangers were using a variation of this type of boat: around thirty foot long, six foot six beam, two foot six deep and capable of carrying over a ton of freight. They were propelled by the early Johnson and Evinrude outboard motors. For personal water transport, the Rangers used canoes.

Lake boats were an extension of the use of rivers as a highway but the larger bodies of water demanded bigger, more seaworthy boats. By 1916 there were boats on Ootsa, Takla and Babine Lakes, all equipped with Evinrude motors; and in 1920 the first of the larger boats appeared in the Nelson district: the *Amabilis* and the *Willow*. In 1921 Cariboo acquired the *Poplar*, Kamloops the *Aspen* and Nelson the *Juniper*, followed by the *Alba* in 1925.

"We have always had patrol boats on the bigger lakes for the use of Rangers," said John Paynter. "Quite often there may be a road up one side of the lake, but this doesn't take care of the other side. Generally the boats have been from twenty to thirty feet long. Originally they were of wood planked construction, then ply, latterly fibreglass and more recently aluminum."

On some lakes there has been an unbroken family line: Kootenay Lake, for instance, acquired the *Amabilis* in 1920, which was replaced in 1928 by the forty foot *Amabilis II* with a 25 h. p. Ballantyne engine. She in turn was replaced in 1952 by the *Amabilis III*, twenty-seven foot ten with a Chrysler Crown engine and a planing hull, previously *We Three*, built in 1948 by Harbour Marine Services of Vancouver. Then in 1970 came the Starcraft *Amabilis IV* with a Mercury inboard/outboard.

"I joined the Forest Service in 1951 as a dispatcher in Fort Fraser," Ron Hawkins told me, "and they used to talk of the old *Tachi*, a riverboat they used in that whole chain of lakes northwest from Stuart Lake, back in the Teens and early Twenties. There are a lot of rapids and bad water around there." In 1926 the *Tachi* was replaced by the *Tachi II*, a narrow thirty-footer built by the Forest Service under the supervision of Jim Blake at Stuart Lake. She lasted through to 1950, when they replaced her with the *Tachi III*, built at the Marine Depot. Finally came the *Tachi IV* in 1970, a fibreglass deep-vee

"followed by the Alba *in 1925."*

with a Mercury tunnel drive for the shallow rivers.

Although the lake waters do not approach Hecate Straits in their gale-lashed frenzy, they can provide some excitement for the Ranger in his small craft. The story is told of the Ranger on the *Amabilis II*, ploughing up Kootenay Lake in a rising gale while the engineer—a devout man—knelt on the deck with hands clasped and head bowed, imploring the Almighty to deliver him from his predicament. This selfish attitude did nothing to reassure the Ranger who—if the engineer's prayers had been answered—would have been left alone to handle the boat.

One of the more unusual of the lake boats was the *Whitesail* on Ootsa, built at the Marine Depot in 1958. At this time Highway 16 was in the process of being upgraded, and in order to get from Prince George to Ootsa Lake a number of Bailey Bridges had to be crossed. The Forest Service decided on an outsize riverboat: forty-five foot long with a cabin, and an eight foot beam to allow it to be hauled over the Bailey Bridges. The lake was littered by debris as a result of the flooding to create a reservoir, so the *Whitesail* was powered by a Hanley Hydrojet from Kermath—the first commercially available marine jet. The engine was a Plymouth Fury 140 h. p. which drove the Hydrojet from its forward end, and from the after end drove a stern-mounted Mercury inboard-outboard unit.

"Both options worked well," said John. "You used the inboard-outboard in clear water, then when you had to come inshore you tipped up the drive leg and connected up the jet. I was present on her first trip on the Lake. We headed for a mat of logs trapped by the trees still standing underwater near the shoreline. The boat rode over the logs and the jet unit gasped for air, but the boat dropped into the water often enough to keep going. We used her like that for twenty years before we sold her."

"One of the most unusual of the lake boats was the Whitesail.*"*

Another option never got off the drawing board. "We were under pressure to try out airscrew-driven boats, such as they use in the Florida Everglades. A man on Babine Lake had such a boat and it was very successful, by all accounts. We happened to have this airscrew-driven snowmobile, so we mounted it on the new *Whitesail* and roared off down the Fraser. We got her up to twelve m.p.h. and began to think the idea had some merit. But while we were in the process of investigating different blade areas, the man on Babine Lake was decapitated by his own propeller, and enthusiasm for such a boat in the Forest Service declined with astonishing rapidity. So we completed the *Whitesail* with inboard power."

* * * * * *

Over the years, roads were built and the use of riverboats declined. There are still one or two of the older riverboats left; they are mainly used by Rangers who need to look at inaccessible timber but lack the funds to use a helicopter.

In the Fifties and Sixties the Forest Service itself began to construct roads into new stands of timber. In many cases access for reconnaissance and surveying was limited to shallow rivers, so the Forest Service began to use jet boats. The first design used the original narrow boats with the rear six feet cut off and a 109 h.p. inboard jet unit installed. A vertical tiller bar was installed amidships and the operator would stand there, scanning the water for obstructions.

"The rivers got very low in summer and we couldn't use propellers," said John. "Although under forty m.p.h. the ram effect improves the performance of the jets, while the drag from the propeller and rudder impedes the screw boats."

In addition to their administrative work in the forests, the Service has been heavily involved in clearing river valleys that were to become reservoirs, and clearing the shorelines of lakes that were to be raised by damming. Large numbers of men with chainsaws were deployed, and perhaps the most important example of this work took place at Lake Williston, which had a considerable fleet based on its waters in the Seventies. Two of the Blimps, the *Cherry II* and the *Silver Fir*, were trucked to the lake for use on inspection work.

Lake work, like coastal work, has its hazards, although of a different nature. On one occasion the *Cherry II* was tied up at the lakeside. One man was working ashore while the other crew member was aboard, preparing the evening meal. Hearing his partner step aboard the cook began to discuss the day's events and their relevance towards the total program, but after a while was struck by the singularly one-sided nature of the exchanges. His partner would only reply in ill-tempered grunts. The cook looked around at the quarterdeck to find a large brown bear pawing at the meat safe, uninterested in the finer points of forestry. With a squeal of fear he fled to the opposite end of the boat, flung open the wheelhouse door and leaped from the bow. The bear meanwhile, also realizing that they did not make a compatible team, had jumped off the stern.

In addition to the two Blimps and sundry smaller craft, two forty-foot tugs operated on Lake Williston: the *Forest Engineer* and the *Forest Mariner*. The former was built in 1965 for use in construction of the High Arrow dam, and the Forest Service bought it in 1968 when it became surplus to requirements at that location. It was so successful that the Forest Service contracted with the same architect for a similar craft, with detail improvements, and in 1972 the *Forest Mariner* was built.

The design was unusual. The hulls were split down the centre line and constructed in two separate halves, with an engine in each half. This made it much easier to transport each tug, on two flatbeds, to Lake Williston where the halves were bolted together. They were used on a variety of duties, and were particularly useful in propelling the Forest Service's eighty-five foot steel transporter barge *LC 15* which ferried D9's, camp equipment, earth-moving equipment, fuel and other supplies to the lake camps.

Williston Lake was a sizeable operation. A small fleet of boomboats was used for assembling logs for sale to the mills at Mackenzie, and three crew

boats were used for taking the men from Mackenzie to the cutting sites around the lakeshore. Two of the crew boats, the *Lake Shore* and the *Forest Shore*, were thirty foot aluminum craft with 200 h. p. Cat 3160 engines with jet drives. Built in 1975, they were the largest aluminum boats used by the Forest Service up to that time. When the Ministry's work on the lake ended, *Lake Shore* was lent to Alcan for use on Ootsa Lake and was finally repossessed as a replacement for *Whitesail* when that boat was sold. *Forest Shore* remained at Mackenzie as a Ranger launch. The third crew boat, *Willow II*, was of similar size with a similar engine, but with a guarded propeller and a steel hull. She was taken over by B. C. Hydro in 1978.

Two floating camps were used on the lake: steel barges with mobile units mounted on them. Camp No. 1 consisted of barges *LC* 12 and 13 with single-storey dwelling units supported by a styrofoam barge, *LC* 8, carrying the power plant. Camp No. 2 was *LC* 16 with two-storey dwellings, supported by *LC* 11 and power plant.

Perhaps the most spectacular item was the burning raft, a large floating ring of steel cylinders supporting a cradle of woven one-inch steel wires. Logs were piled into the cradle and ignited, and once a good hot fire took hold it was possible for barge-mounted cranes to add wet debris straight from the lake and keep the fire burning indefinitely, while the ash fell through the wires to the bottom of the lake. Finally, in 1978 B. C. Hydro took over the work, and the camps, barges and boats passed into their hands with the exception of *Forest Engineer* and *Forest Mariner*, which were sold.

Experience over the years has shaped the lake boats to their present form typified by the *Peace Ranger* at Hudson's Hope. She is thirty feet long, constructed of fabricated welded aluminum which has proved by far the most durable material for the purpose, jet propelled because of floating debris, with a Cat 3208 turbo diesel engine for power, economy and safety. She may lack some of the romance of the old wooden boats, but her crew appreciate the speed and comfort.

There is still room for individuality, however.

"The newest dam, the Revelstoke 1880, will flood out our Ranger Station at Mica Creek," John said. "Rather than build a Ranger Station elsewhere, we opted for a vessel which forestry crews could live aboard spending a week at a time at the worksite. I stumbled across a vessel at Sechelt which suited the requirements. She's forty-five foot long with a fifteen foot two beam and weighs sixteen tons, and she was named the *Curious* by Gordon Hall, who built her

"In 1972 the Forest Mariner *was built."*

as a houseboat in his own aluminum fabricating shop. The welding was good and the fitting out was excellent too, so we bought her and trucked her up to the Mica Dam. We named her the *Kinbasket Forest*. We can operate eight to ten people from her. She has double beds which were not entirely suitable for our purpose because although we do on occasion carry both sexes, they are not necessarily nocturnally compatible."

Only John could have produced that last sentence in the course of a serious discourse on the new aluminum craft; straight-faced, too.

"It's the end of an era," John said, not for the first time. He's retired now, and my incessant jogging of his memory tended to make him maudlin. "The era ended with the *Coast Ranger*, and I suppose it should have ended earlier. Wooden boats are a lost cause in these days of high maintenance costs. Fibreglass, steel and aluminum lend themselves to mass production, prefabrication and so on. That's where the future lies, I'm afraid. That, and helicopters."

Helicopters have been used by the Forest Service marine arm for some time, in fact. The *Hecate Ranger*, the *Forest Surveyor* and the *Forest Cruiser* are all equipped for towing helicopter-barges.

The *Forest Surveyor* has an interesting history. She was originally built for the Army as one of thirteen halibut-type hulls known as the *Combat* design after the prototype. In 1946 she was offered for sale as *Colonel Ward*, and the Forest Service bought her for $15,000. The *Syrene* towed her back to the Maintenance Depot. After one summer's use in her original condition she was rebuilt at Star Shipyard to increase accommodation ready for the days when she would be pulling the scow and helicopter, with an Inventory crew on board.

"We extended the wheelhouse aft," said Tommy Edwards, "and built a new wheelhouse on top." He sniffed. "It was the skippers that wanted the high wheelhouse, and then they complained about the rolling, so we had to load more ballast in. Hell, they didn't know what heavy weather is. During the war that boat had seen service in the Aleutians, where you get real weather . . ."

Norm Beazley skippered the *Surveyor* shortly after the new wheelhouse was installed. He took a crew up to the Charlottes to do inventory work. "The ballast had made her very stable and she did excellent work. She could carry an Inventory crew of thirteen people plus the ship's crew. That would be in the late Sixties . . ." He chuckled, remembering. "Once, going into Naden Harbour, the tide was high. It's a very narrow channel and the tide runs to beat hell; you've got all that expanse of Naden Harbour and an entrance possibly a hundred feet wide where the tide roars in and out. Anyway, I misjudged the distance off the shore and put her on the gravel bar. Then the tide got right under her and laid her on her beam ends. I put her in full astern and worked her round so she was heading out, and gunned the hell out of her. She came off and came upright, throwing gravel all over the place. All the kids from the In-

". . . equipped for towing helicopter barges."

ventory crew were on deck by now, giving me a bad time.

"So I looked down on them from the height of the wheelhouse and I said sorrowfully, 'It's the last bloody time I'm going to do that. Here I've gone to the trouble to give you an emergency exercise and just one man, the cook, came up with his lifejacket on. How many times have I told you always to wear lifejackets if you think there's trouble? From now on you can drown, for all I care!' All bullshit, of course. I don't know whether they believed it or not."

The principle behind Norm Beazley's approach is similar to that used by Jack McNeill, a proud, dour Scot who ran hard aground at Alberni, where the Somass River comes out. Naturally enough, he didn't want any logger to see the Ranger stuck, so he shored up the boat as the tide fell, then jumped out and pretended to be cleaning and copper-painting the bottom until the tide came in again.

Another crew boat was the *Forest Cruiser*, bought in 1956. In the words of the Newsletter: "It is hoped that with the acquisition of this fine vessel the Headquarters cruising party will now have a mobile headquarters on a year round basis . . . Since approximately two-thirds of the timber-sale applications in the Vancouver Forest District require boat transportation, the *Forest Cruiser* should assist in providing much better service to logging operators . . . "

She was sixty foot long with a beam of thirteen foot six, powered by a 165 h. p. Gray diesel which gave her a speed of eight and a half knots. She had accommodation for ten people including a ship's crew of three, and was pre-

viously owned by Captain Higgs of Nanaimo under the name of *Marine Explorer*. Earlier still, as Newsletter puts it: "There have been sordid allusions to this vessel being used as a rum-runner in bygone days. We do not, however, expect any further trouble along these lines with the stalwarts of our cruising party."

"She was a nice boat," said Norm Beazley. "When I had her, she was taking out forestry crews who did the surveying for planting jobs. She had a semi-planing hull, although with the power the Forest Service put in her she'd never get on the plane. Originally she had a diesel in the centre for normal use, with a big gas engine mounted on either side for use when the law was after her.

"She had a winch on her and we used to tow a barge—the *LC6*—as a helicopter pad. Even when we were running the helicopter could come in and land. We used it to drop guys up in the inaccessible areas of mountains.

"She used to pound in a head sea because she couldn't get her bows up. I was heading down the coast from Tofino into a south-easter once, and the cook came up to me and said, 'I think we're sinking,' which isn't popular news, in a heavy blow. I went down into the galley, and sure enough the water was swishing all over hell down there. I went into the engine room and switched the bilge pumps on; they didn't work too well but I got one of them going and it kept up with the water. We ran around the south of Vancouver Island like that, and across to the Marine Depot in a hard south-east blow. When we arrived the ways were busy but I said, 'You'd better get her up there. I don't think she'll float till morning.'

"She'd stripped one of the garboard planks, next to the keel. She was an old boat, and her planks tended to work. When she reared up in that sea she must have buckled a bit, and popped this plank right off. No wonder the water was coming in. But they fixed her, and she came out good as new."

* * * * * *

In addition to administration work, timber cruising, scaling and road and bridge-building, the Forest Service has long been involved in planting work. Over the years a series of landing craft have been used for transporting tree seedlings, equipment and men, of which the best known is probably the *LC5*.

LC5 was built in 1944 by Dominion Construction of Vancouver, with a length of fifty two foot three and a beam of eighteen feet. Initially she saw service as RCAF No. M.645 until, surplus to requirements, she was sold to

Cangold Mining in 1949. They took her by logging railroad to Great Central Lake on Vancouver Island where she spent the next 14 years. She passed through various hands over the following years, including the B. C. Power Commission and B. C. Forest Products Ltd. Eventually the Forest Service bought her for use in planting the fire-ravaged hillsides above the lake.

She entered salt water for the first time in 1951 having been trucked to the Somass River and thence to the Pacific. "Don Adams took her down the west coast of the Island and across to the Depot, escorted by Captain McKay in the *Forest Surveyor*," Tommy Edwards told me. "It was an exciting trip. McKay nicknamed Don Adams 'Captain Courageous' after that."

For a long time *LC*5 was used by Engineering Branch for road-building and maintenance, and they used her to the limit. Norm Beazley recalls one trip from Port McNeill to the Kingcome River with a D6 Cat on board. "That Cat was a monster. We had to run half-speed all the way because the bow was taking on water half-way up the deck . . . Normally she'd handle all right, though. We'd have a few problems when she'd fill up with water in the side pockets; she'd work a bit and start leaking when we were coming down against a heavy south-easter, for instance. She'd pound to beat the devil with her blunt front end. It would jar your teeth out."

Tommy Edwards told of her later days. "They were hitting the beach up at Kingcome Inlet, and we were having to do a lot of maintenance. Eventually she began to sink with a grader on her. We beached her, got the water out, and filled her with styrofoam. Finally, when we got the *Forest Transporter*, we scrapped her. We took the engines out and towed her to a place where they burn the river debris, and put the torch to her."

Her replacement, the *Forest Transporter*, was a fine vessel. Steel-hulled, eighty-three foot four long with a twenty-eight foot beam, she was built in 1974 at McKenzie Barge and Marine Ways Ltd., in North Van. "They put in two Chrysler Nissan V8's, which was the lowest bid — the old problem," said Tom bitterly. "We had them for a year and they gave all kinds of trouble. I pushed for two Jimmy V12's which we should have had in the first place; we'd had them in the *Forest Engineer* and *Forest Mariner*. In the end they let us have them, and we've had no problems since."

Initially the *Transporter* was frequently used for transporting seedlings to planting sites of the coast. She was a handy vessel for the work, because she could carry the planters' camp too, if required. On one occasion when her services would have prevented a lot of grief, however, she was not available . . .

"*The* Forest Transporter *was a fine vessel.*"

"We had to plant 800,000 trees to a rigid schedule at Kingcome River," Russ Campbell said. "Unfortunately they lifted the seedlings at Campbell River nursery a little before we expected, and they began to go mouldy in the boxes. So we had to get them planted as soon as possible. The *Forest Transporter* was elsewhere at the time, and couldn't be used, so we had to rent a local barge.

"We couldn't get a tug, so we had to tow the barge with the *Nesika*. We loaded the barge at Kelsey Bay. It hadn't carried so much weight for twenty years and all the planking had opened up above the normal waterline. It was dark before we headed up Johnstone Strait, and after a while we noticed that the barge was starting to go down. So we put it on a beach and unloaded some of the trees, anchored the *Nesika* and waited for the tide to come in."

By this time it was the middle of the night, so Russ and his men sat drinking coffee and discussing their predicament. Clearly the barge was not going to carry the trees to the Kingcome River; she would go down long before that. Tired and miserable, they considered alternatives. There were no further barges available, so the only hope was a floatplane.

At some point, someone looked out of the porthole and saw a light. "We were damned sure there were no lights in view when we dropped the hook," said Russ. "So we got out the charts, and the nearest light to our position was Windy Point, about ten miles away. It was about that time when we realized we were drifting up the Strait . . . Well, if you've ever tried to find a barge that was up on a beach in the middle of the night, anywhere up to ten miles away, and you've got nothing but a spotlight to look for it with . . . " He laughed. "It's not easy, I can tell you. And we were panicking because we'd transferred a fair amount of the load to the beached end of the barge, and so when the tide came in the barge would float off and sink by the bow, and that would be the end of the trees."

But they found it, an hour and a half later. They reloaded it and towed it back to Kelsey Bay, got pumps going, and chartered an aircraft to ferry the trees to the head of Kingcome. Their troubles were not over, however.

"It was a single engined Otter. The pilot was watching his floats as we loaded her. 'If it'll float, it'll fly,' he said. When the floats were half awash he took a long run, struggled into the air and headed for Kingcome.

"He landed in the river and taxied along on the float steps, and everything was fine. Then he cut the power to come into the dock. And he'd forgotten that he'd loaded her to the maximum in salt water, but now he was in fresh water. By gosh, the aircraft started to go down! So he gunned her up, and he finished up on the beach too!"

* * * * * *

John Paynter was also involved in a sinking episode. The *Catherine Graham* was at one time a Department of Highways ferry. She was seventy feet long and thirty feet wide and was named after a baby born on board the *Moniker*, her predecessor on the Denman Island run. This appealed to John's sentimental instinct, so when the Forest Service fell heir to her he left the name as it was.

In the spring of 1970, shortly after her acquisition, she was fitted with a heavier bow ramp at Nanaimo for handling reforestation contractors' equipment in the Bella Coola area. It was a beautifully calm day when John, Captain Robinson and Barry Hendrickson left Nanaimo harbour in the *Catherine Graham*, bound for the Marine Depot.

The first inkling of trouble came shortly after they reached open water and noticed that the deck seemed to be tilting forward, and water was creeping up it towards them. At first they assumed that this was simply the effect of the rougher water in the Straits. "So we didn't pay much attention to it," said John. "But later when we got into calmer water we realized something was seriously amiss; the deck was awash and it wasn't just waves. We opened up the forepeak and sure enough, there was water in there very nearly up to deck level. There was a watertight bulkhead, but Barry thought the boat was ballasted with rock, which might loosen and crash through it. He kept looking at the lifeboat.

"It became a matter of fine calculation whether the bow would sink so far that the propeller would come out of the water, rendering the vessel unmanoeuverable. In which case we would have had to be towed ignominiously up the Fraser River stern first."

As it was they made it to the Marine Depot with the propeller thrashing at the surface of the water and drawing comment from passing vessels. "We tried to look nonchalant about the whole thing as though this was an everyday occurrence, but we knew we must look pretty ridiculous. When we got her pumped out we took a dinghy and rowed carefully along the bow, examining the new welds, and sure enough we found a hole. It was only an inch long and a quarter inch wide, but we'd taken about eight tons of water aboard."

The perils of the sea can surface from the most unexpected quarters. One day Wilf Archer received a message that the *Alpine Fir II* had been struck in the stern by a fishboat while tied up at the dock, and had lost part of her taffrail in addition to suffering some damage to the woodwork. At the first opportunity he set off for Kelsey Bay to inspect the boat.

While Wilf was examining the damage, an uproar broke out on a nearby boat. Struggling figures could be seen and eventually one man, bigger than the others, broke free and, shouting with rage, strode down the dock towards Wilf. Puzzled and not a little alarmed, Wilf turned to face him.

There was no satisfactory explanation at that time. Incoherent with temper, the man threw Wilf into the ocean.

It was the injustice as much as the cold water which upset Wilf, particularly when he tried to climb out, and the man pushed him back in. Whatever crime

Wilf had committed against the man, it appeared to carry the death penalty. It is in such moments that a man sees his destiny most clearly and, realizing the situation had passed the point where reasoned discussion might prevail, Wilf seized the man by the legs and pulled him in too.

For a while they thrashed there, then the man's companions arrived, pulled them both out and began to apologize to Wilf. It appeared that Wilf's assailant was the fisherman who had rammed the *Alpine Fir*. Seeing Wilf inspecting the boat, he had jumped to the conclusion that the Forest Service were going to accuse him of causing the damage.

Wilf had to admit that was a reasonable assumption.

The others told Wilf it was a sad case, because the fisherman had not been quite himself at the moment of impact, being under the influence of drugs.

The discussion continued for some time until the wet clothes of the combatants began to cool their enthusiasm, and Wilf left.

"That fisherman had kind of an unreasonable attitude," Wilf told me mildly. "After all, two of our people had helped him dock his boat after the accident, and he'd never have been able to do it by himself."

Forest Service men take such incidents in their stride, however, and there is no better example of this than the reaction of Kerry Neave, the *Alpine Fir's* engineer. "Hey, Wilf," he said afterwards. "While you were underwater, did you see any sign of our taffrail?"

* * * * * *

Sadly, there was the occasional fatality. Some years ago Ken Halliday spent the week in the Tribune Channel area on his Blimp. He'd finished the week's work and he had his wife and children on board with him; they intended to anchor at the beach at the top of Bond Sound for the night and maybe pick some oysters, then head back to Chatham Channel the next day, Saturday.

As Ken was picking his spot for anchoring, one of the kiddies tumbled overboard. Without thinking, Ken jumped in. Treading water, he passed the child to his wife on deck, but then sank and was seen no more.

"I was having a barbecue in our back yard in North Vancouver," Don Owen said, "when I got a call from Search and Rescue saying they'd intercepted a radio call from a woman who was very distraught, on one of our boats. We got hold of a Beaver and flew up to Bond Sound at first light, taking a diver from Alert Bay. He couldn't find anything so I went back to Vancouver and arranged for two men from the North Van volunteer firemen scuba club.

When we got back to Bond Sound a pod of killer whales were going through, and naturally enough divers don't like to go down with them around. So we loaded the Beaver up with rocks and bombed them. They left the Sound, but whether we had anything to do with it I don't know. The divers went down, and recovered the body within twenty minutes.

"Apart from the distress of the wife and children, one of the saddest things was the wheelhouse of the Blimp. Ken's lifejacket was hanging at the doorway. You don't spend time putting a lifejacket on when your kid falls in the water."

EPILOGUE

Over the months, the old boats had come to life in my mind; they had births, lives, characters, and sometimes deaths. It was natural that I began to wonder what had happened to the ones which were described in the files as 'disposed of'.

I began to watch the harbours for old boats. By now I had memorized the appearance of many of the older Forest Service boats from the original photographs. I carried my camera. I looked for the characteristic Forest Service shape; something like a troller, but with an aftercabin. I began to build up an album of photographs: boats I had seen and recorded on film, but which were still unidentified. Some of them may have been old Forest Service boats, others undoubtedly were not. It was often difficult to catch the owner on board. I started leaving my telephone number pushed into cracks on cabin doors.

In July of 1981 I sighted another possibility — a double-ender of around forty feet tied up in the Inner Harbour at Victoria. The owners were not on board. I took a photograph and left a note. In due course the roll of film was developed and printed, and the shot of the double-ender came out well: white hull, green upperworks and the name *Don Bar B.*

Don Bar B.

I knew that name.

I searched through my notes. Eventually I found what I was looking for: a one-line note taken from an old file at the Marine Station:

"1961 — Sold to W. A. Blair, New Westminster. New name: *Don Bar B.*"

The file was that of the original *Oliver Clark.*

A week later she lay at a private wharf on Piers Island, opposite the tip of the Saanich Peninsula and clearly visible from my living room window. She had been there for a few days before I realized who she was, and sailed over there, and took another photograph. She lay there for a week or more. My easy chair faced that way, and in the evenings when the sun set behind Saltspring Island the last rays caught her windows and lit them up like fire.

*　*　*　*　*　*

"I took another photograph."

Epilogue

"And that about wraps it up," I said.

"What do you mean?" asked John Paynter, startled.

"I mean the book's finished. What better ending could I have? Rediscovery of the old *Oliver Clark*. The sunset. Windows like fire."

"Yes, but what about all the other boats?" John said plaintively. "You've only talked about the big ones. There are dozens more, all with interesting histories. You hardly touched on the lake boats, for instance."

"If I put any more boats in the book, I won't have room for the people. The people are as important as the boats, remember."

He tried to pin me down. "About the people, then. You kept raising the mystery of Oliver Clark, but then you left it all in the air. The reader won't be satisfied with that. He'll want to know what really happened at that fire at Port Neville. He'll want more than sunsets on portholes, for heaven's sake."

"I have more."

"Like what?"

"Would you be satisfied with a second-hand eyewitness account?"

"It would be better than what we've had so far."

So I told him what a retired Forest Service man had told me concerning the events of June 25th., 1925 . . .

*   *   *   *   *   *

The fire at Port Neville was under control, so it seemed. The firefighting crew were mopping up around the fringes. Then the wind shifted, fanning the flames towards the small settlement nearby. The inhabitants were evacuated to the beach. The firefighting crew redoubled their efforts, joined at this point by Oliver Clark.

It became apparent that the fire was again out of control. Worse, it was spreading rapidly through the bush bordering the beach. Within minutes the men were cut off, trapped in a ring of fire.

A quick decision had to be made. Clark, in charge of operations, made it. They would make a run through the blazing forest to the beach.

But the men objected. They reasoned that the fire was burning most fiercely in that direction. Further inland, they pointed out, it was showing signs of burning itself out. An argument ensued—the last thing anybody wanted, in a time of dire emergency.

Finally, as the flames closed in, Oliver Clark ran for the beach.

The rest of the crew, equally convinced of the correctness of their decision, ran inland. Dodging through the blazing scrub, their clothing began to smoulder with the heat, they finally reached the burned-over area. Here, scorched and coughing their hearts up, they rested. Their decision had been right—just.

Oliver Clark, heading in the opposite direction, died from his burns.

*   *   *   *   *   *

"Heroes are necessary," Louie Lorentsen once told me. "They help build morale. Compared with General Custer and Davy Crockett, Oliver Clark may well have been a brave man. There have been brave stunts pulled all through the years by our staff. It's bound to happen, with the kind of country we operate in. People drown. People get killed in firefighting accidents. It's part of the job, and we accept it."

In February 1976, a Beaver floatplane was trying to land at Ucluelet in a snowstorm. In zero visibility, with waves running up to ten feet high in the open sea, the pilot finally found calmer waters. On his final approach, however, he was forced to bank sharply left to avoid a shoal. The plane hit the water at an angle. The port float was torn off. As the plane began to sink, the pilot and four passengers climbed out and, treading water, hung onto a wing.

Fred Parris, a passenger, called out, "Can everybody swim?"

Epilogue

One man said, "No."

Fred was the only one with a lifejacket. He inflated it and helped the other man into it.

The group started swimming towards the distant shore, all except Fred Parris who was seen making his way back to the plane, probably to fetch more lifejackets. He'd been trained that way. Unlike the others he was an experienced seaman.

He was never seen again.

The others reached shore and were all rescued.

Fred Parris was a black Jamaican. He was a relief Forest Service skipper, heading for Tofino to take charge of the *Forest Cruiser* which was operating temporarily on the west coast of the island.

It is very probable that he was a hero.

*   *   *   *   *   *

I climbed the stairs into the loft of the Marine Station. There was a lot of old stuff there, they told me. Historical junk that would shortly be shipped to the Forest Museum in Duncan. Maybe I'd find something of interest, they said.

The air was warm up here, and smelled of paint. Daylight filtered through skylights and windows covered with a quarter century of grime. Outside, the flat riverside meadows were misty with rain. Faint shouts came up the stairs; unintelligible instructions and the rasping of a file on metal. The vast room was lined with benches; once it had been an armoury of Bennett-McDonald pumps, waiting like timebombs. The cupboards were a particularly bilious shade of green—probably Seafoam Green useful for painting families. On one bench a great stack of old oars lay like driftwood.

The museum specimens were piled in the centre of the floor. Two ancient bicycles, green and lettered B. C. FORESTRY. An abundance of used mattresses suggesting a thousand wakeful nights wondering whether the anchor was dragging. Boxes of old stuff: old trophies, copies of the 'Root and Branch', pieces of wood with labels on them, pieces of machinery equally enigmatic, old posters. Dusty photograph albums . . .

I began to leaf through them.

Endless pictures of trees in varying stages of growth. Trees young and fluffy, trees old and scrawny, trees horizontal and dead. Groups of men standing outside log cabins, scowling ferociously. Boats . . .

The *Kiora*, surging through the log breakwater at Thurston Bay. The *Beatrice R* on placid waters, the *Euclataw* under a waterfall at Toba Inlet. "1915. Engineer Fisk on deck, A. H. Black with pike pole, Frank Carlin at bow." The *Sitka Spruce* on the ways, the launching of the *Cottonwood*. Thurston Bay under construction, Thurston Bay complete, Thurston Bay in flames. A man resting on a log...

He looks terribly tired, and he wears no clothes. The log lies on a beach and the waters beyond are quiet, and a distant hillside is hazy with smoke. The log obscures the lower half of the man. His shoulders are slumped. His neck, thin and vulnerable, droops and his face rests on the rough bark, his hands crossed in front so that his forehead is pillowed on his wrists. His right hand is clearly empty but his left might have something in it. Then again, it might not. He looks very young, very defenceless.

The caption reads: "Body of Oliver Clark who lost his life in the Port Neville fire on June 25th, 1925. Photograph taken 8.10 p. m. on that date."

The photograph is so simple and tragic that it forbids speculation. There is nothing in it that was not wrought by nature. There is a log, a beach, waters, a hillside and a dead human animal, naked. It is elemental, and terrifying.

Looking at it, I don't give a damn whether Oliver Clark died with his badge in his hand or not. It simply doesn't matter. He died.

He died like Fred Parris and others died, while doing his job, while earning his pay. Not duty. Not heroism. These are abstract symbols invented by Man for his own sophisticated purposes. What matters is the deal a man makes: for this amount of pay, he will do this work and take these risks in order to do it. On the credit side, we must add the enjoyment he gets out of the job. On the debit, we must enter the possibility of dying.

Many thousands of men have made this simple deal with the Forest Service over the years. They would be embarrassed if it was suggested that there is a certain amount of heroism involved every time they point their bows into an oncoming storm in Hecate Strait, or ride the tide through Okisollo Channel, or undertake an errand of mercy when the wind is slicing the tops off the waves in Johnstone Strait and night is darkening the eastern sky. They would point out, as Louie Lorentsen points out:

It's a part of the job, and we accept it.

We wish them a safe passage.

Epilogue

Name	Date Built	Date Acq.	Builders	Mat'l	Metres LOA	B	D	Date Disposed	Comments
Adam Lake									Adams Lake
Alanbee	1910	1910		Wood	12.8	3.0	1.2	1926	
Alba		1925		Wood					
Alder	1921	1921	Hoffar Bros., Vancouver	Wood	9.1	2.4	.8	1947	Damaged by fire, 1922. Blimp
Alder II	1949	1949	F.S.M.D.	Wood	10.5	2.7	.9	1978	2nd Series Blimp
Aleli				Wood					
Alpine Fir	1926		Prince Rupert Dry Dock	Wood	12.2	2.9		1947	Damaged by explosion 1927.
Alpine Fir II	1947	1949	G. H. Oliver, North Van.	Wood	13.2	3.5		In Service	Ex 'Letitia II'
Amabilis	1920			Wood					
Amabalis II	1928	1928	Erikson Bros., Vancouver	Wood	12.2	3.0	.9	1947	
Amabilis III	1948	1952	Harbour Marine Service, Vancouver	Wood	8.5	3.0			Ex 'We Three' -Kootenay Lake
Amabilis IV	1970	1970	Starcraft	Alum.	6.4	2.3		In Service	Kootenay Lake
Arbutus	1921	1921	Hoffar Brothers, Vancouver	Wood	9.1	2.4	.8	1947	Blimp
Arbutus II	1949	1949	F.S.M.D.	Wood	10.5	2.7	.9	In Service	2nd Series Blimp
Arbutus III	1970	1970		F.G.	5.5	2.3		In Service	
Aspen	1921	1921		Wood					
Aspen II	1947		Falconer Marine	Wood	4.9	1.6			Babine Lake
Aspen II	1969			F.G.	5.5	2.4		In Service	Babine Lake
Balsam	1921	1921	Hoffar Brothers, Vancouver	Wood	9.1	2.4	.8		Blimp

Balsam (II)	1944	1949	Bird & Nicholson, Victoria	Wood	12.8	3.7			Ex 'Betty Lou'
Balsam III	1973			F.G.	5.7	2.3		In Service	
B.C. Forester	1923	1923	F.S. (Thurston Bay)	Wood	16.9	3.9	2.1	1936	Lengthened 1935, Rebuilt 1943 - F.S.M.D.
B.C. Scaler	1944	1951	Stephens Bros., Stockton, Calif.	Wood	18.6	4.6		1977	Ex U.S.N. Rescue Craft, Ex Flying Saucer
Beatrice R.	1913	1913	Hinton Electric Co., Victoria	Wood	11.0	2.9	1.2		Rebuilt - F.S.M.D. 1941
Birch	1921	1921	V. M. Dafoe, Vancouver	Wood					
Birch II	1928			Wood					
Birch III	1941	1943	E. Wall, Prince Rupert	Wood	8.5	2.8	.8	1970	
Birch IV	1971	1971	F.S. (Thurston Bay)	F.G.	5.6	2.2		In Service	Ex 'John Lloyd'
A. L. Bryant	1928	1928	Marine Transit Co.	Wood	12.8	2.9		1950	Rebuilt at F.S.M.D. 1942. Sunk 1950
Catherine Graham	1954	1970		Steel	21.3	9.1		1975	Ex Denman Is. Ferry
P.Z. Caverhill	1929	1936		Wood	21.9	3.8		1941	Ex Rum-runner 'Yurinohana'
Check Scaler	1924	1924	F.S. (Thurston Bay)	Wood	9.1	2.4	1.1		Blimp
Cherry	1922	1922	Hoffar Brothers, Vancouver	Wood	9.1	2.4	.8		Blimp
Cherry II	1946	1946	F.S.M.D.	Wood	10.5	2.7	.9	1978	2nd Series Blimp
Chestnut	1924	1924	F.S. (Thurston Bay)	Wood	7.6	2.3			
Chilako IV	1959			Steel	6.4	2.2			
Clayoquot Forest	1978	1978	Sangster	F.G.	7.0	2.4		In Service	Tug
Coast Ranger	1967	1967	F.S.M.D.	Wood	14.7	4.0		In Service	
Columbia Ranger	1974	1974		Alum.	9.1	3.0		In Service	
Conifer				Wood				In Service	

Name	Date Built	Date Acq.	Builders	Mat'l	LOA	B	D	Date Disposed	Comments
Conifer II	1941		Ex R.C.A.F. — P.C. Benson Shipyard	Wood	11.4	2.4			Ex R.C.A.F. 'Teal'
Conifer III	1975	1978	West Bay Ship-builders, Vancouver	Steel	9.1	3.0		1976	
Cottonwood	1922	1922	Erickson & Ball	Wood	11.6	2.9			
Cottonwood II	1952	1952	F.S.M.D.	Wood	10.5	2.7	.9	1978	2nd Series Blimp
Cowichan Forest	1976	1976	Hourston	F.G.	7.0	2.7		In Service	
Cypress	1927			Wood	7.6	2.1			
Dean Ranger	1959	1965	Star Shipyard	Wood	13.3	3.8		In Service	Ex 'Otter II'
Departure Bay	1926	1945	Nanaimo	Wood	16.5	4.3	2.0	1950	Ex Navy
Diavno	1939	1953	Walter Boat Works, Nelson	Wood	7.6	2.4	.7		Babine Lake
Dogwood	1938	1939	Boeing, Vancouver	Wood	11.1	3.0	1.5	1958	Ex 'Fish-Trap'
Douglas Fir	1918	1918	F.S. (Thurston Bay)	Wood	9.7	2.6	1.1		
Douglas Fir II	1947	1947	F.S.M.D.	Wood	10.5	2.7	.9		2nd Series Blimp
Elder	1947	1947	Falconer Marine	Wood	4.9	1.6			Interior Lake
Elmera	1923			Wood	11.3				
Embree	1909	1918	New Brunswick	Wood	11.2	3.1	1.3	1930	
Euclataw	1913	1913	Hinton Electric, Victoria	Wood	16.5	3.5	2.0		
Eunice B.	1914	1914	Hinton Electric, Victoria	Wood	11.0	2.9	1.2		
Eva R	1913	1913	Hinton Electric, Victoria	Wood				1949	
Eve				Wood	11.0	2.9	1.2	1939	
Export Patrol		1918		Wood	8.2			1920	
Faloma		1912		Wood				1917	
Francis Lynn	1970	1970	Fibreform	F.G.	8.7	2.4		In Service	Ex 'Mountain Ash III'

					L	B	D		
Forest Assistant				Wood	10.7			1974	Tug, Ex 'Barnston Island', Rebuilt F.S.M.D. 1962
Forest Cruiser	1932	1956	F.S.M.D.	Wood	18.3	4.0		1976	Ex 'Marine Explorer'
Forest Dispatcher	1960	1960	Benson Brothers, Vancouver	Wood	11.9	3.4		In Service	
Forest Engineer	1965	1968		Steel	10.9	4.9		1978	Tug
Forest Mariner	1972	1972	Vito Shipyard, Delta	Steel	10.9	5.2		978	Tug
Forest Pioneer	1948		A. R. Benson Shipyard, Vancouver	Wood	11.9	3.1		1976	Tug - Ex 'Clayhurst'
Forest Ranger	1937		Victoria Boat Repair Works	Wood	14.9	3.4	1.5		
Forest Ranger II	1953	1953	F.S.M.D.	Wood	13.4	3.7		In Service	
Forest Scout	1970	1970	Sangster, Vancouver	F.G.	6.7	2.0		In Service	
Forest Shore	1975	1975	Shore Boatbuilders, N.W.	Alum.	9.1	2.7		In Service	
Forest Supervisor	1955	1955	F.S.M.D.	Wood	9.8	2.9		In Service	
Forest Surveyor	1944	1946	A. C. Benson Shipyard, Vancouver	Wood	16.5	4.9	2.1	In Service	Ex 'Colonel Ward'
Forest Transporter	1974	1974	MacKenzie Barge, N. Vancouver	Steel	25.4	8.5		In Service	
Forest Voyageur	1975		Voyageur Aluminum Products, Port Moody	Alum.	9.1	2.7		In Service	
Geraldine R.	1913	1913	Hinton Electric Co., Victoria	Wood	11.0	2.9	1.2	1923	Burned and sunk
Gleam	1918			Wood	12.2				
Gwen	1914			Wood	7.9				
Hazel	1950	1950	F.S.M.D.	Wood	6.2	2.2	.6		
Hazel II	1968			F.G.	5.9	2.4			
Heather	1949			Wood	5.9	1.2	.5	In Service	Ex 'Seatime'

Name	Date Built	Date Acq.	Builders	Mat'l	LOA	B	D	Date Disposed	Comments
					Metres				
Hecate Ranger	1962	1962	West Coast Salvage, Vancouver	Wood	18.7	5.2		In Service	
Hemlock	1925		Mortimer & Knight	Wood	12.2	2.9	1.0		
Herring	1914			Wood					
Hermes	1969			Wood					
Holly			B.C. Fibreglass, N. Vancouver	F.G.	5.5	2.4		In Service	
Idonno				Wood	9.8				
Island Scaler	1971		West Bay Steel & Boat Works, Delta	F.G.	10.4	3.7		In Service	
Jean L.		1914		Wood					Powell Lake
Juniper		1922		Wood					Ex 'Maureen'
Juniper II				Wood					
Juniper III	1948	1948	Falconer Marine Ltd.	Wood	7.9	2.4	.9	Circa 1969	
Juniper IV	1970	1970	Hourston	F.G.	6.1	2.3		In Service	
Kay				Wood					
Kinbasket Forest		1982	Gordon Hall	Alum.	13.7	4.6	.6	In Service	
Kingcome Forest	1978	1978	Sangster	F.G.	7.0	2.4		In Service	
Kiora	1910	1910	Victoria	Wood	11.3	3.2	1.3		
Kyuquot Forest	1976	1976	Hourston	F.G.	7.0	2.7		In Service	
Lake Shore	1975	1975	Shore Boat Builders, N.W.	Alum.	9.1	2.7		In Service	
Larch				Wood					
Larch		1937	Scott Payne	Wood	10.7	2.4	.9	1949	Ex 'Madrona'
Larch II	1946	1949	F.S.M.D.	Wood	7.3	2.4	.5		Ex 'Atonic'
Larch III	1967			Wood	7.9	2.4		In Service	
Laurel	1936	1942	Walker & Vanderson	Wood	8.5	2.3	.8		Ex 'Nelda'

Name			Builder	Material			Status	Notes
Laurel II								
Laurel III	1967	1967	F.S.M.D.	Wood	9.1	2.4	In Service	
L.C. 1	1947		U.S. Government	Wood	11.0	3.3		
L.C. 2	1946			Wood	11.0	3.3		
L.C. 3	1948			Wood	11.0	3.3		
L.C. 4	1949			Wood	11.0	3.3		
L.C. 5	1944	1949	Dominion Construction, Vancouver	Wood	15.9	5.5		Ex 'Cangold'
L.C. 6	1954			Wood	18.3	4.9	In Service	
L.C. 7	1961	1961	F.S.M.D.	Wood	17.1	8.5	1975	
L.C. 8				Wood/ Styro	14.0	6.4	In Service	
L.C. 9	1955	1955	F.S.M.D.	Wood/ Styro	13.7	6.4	1979	
L.C. 10	1946	1963	Bel-Aire Shipyard, Vancouver	Steel	21.3	7.3	In Service	
L.C. 11	1961			Steel	17.1	9.1	1978	
L.C. 12	1966	1966	Bel-Aire Shipyard, Vancouver	Steel	17.1	9.1	1978	
L.C. 13	1966	1966	Bel-Aire Shipyard, Vancouver	Steel	17.1	9.1	1978	
L.C. 14	1975			Steel	17.1	9.1	1978	Ex Harrop Ferry
L.C. 15	1970	1970	Nanaimo	Steel	24.3	8.9	1978	Ex Clayhurst Ferry
L.C. 16	1970	1970	Nahanni Ind., Port Mann	Steel	24.4	9.8	1978	
L.C. 17	1972	1972	Sealander, Vancouver	F.G.	7.3	2.7	In Service	
L.C. 18	1973	1973	Sealander, Vancouver	F.G.	7.3	2.8	1976	
L.C. 19	1973	1974	Sealander, Vancouver	F.G.	7.5	2.8	In Service	Ex Arrowhead Ferry
L.C. 20	1960	1974	John Manly, Vancouver	Steel	15.8		In Service	
L.C. 21	1970	1974	John Manly, Vancouver	Steel	15.8		In Service	

Name	Date Built	Date Acq.	Builders	Mat'l	LOA	B	D	Date Disposed	Comments
						Metres			
L.C. 22	1967	1976		Steel	12.2	12.2		1978	
L.C. 23	1974	1974	Sealander, Vancouver	F.G.	7.3			In Service	
Leila R.	1913	1913	Hinton Electric Co., Victoria	Wood	16.5	3.5	2.0	1925	
Lillian D.	1925	1925	Prince Rupert Dry Dock Co.	Wood	18.3	3.8	1.6		Rebuilt 1942 - F.S.M.D.
Lodgepole	1953	1953	F.S.M.D.	Wood	7.9	2.7			
Lodgepole II	1970	1970	B.C. Fibreglass, Vancouver	F.G.	5.2	2.1	1.2	1981	
Mac				Wood					Harrison Lake
Madrona				Wood				1942	
Madrona II	1947	1949	Falconer Marine	Wood	7.9	2.7			Ex 'Ow-Wahla'
Madrona III	1971		Fibreform, Kelowna	F.G.	7.3	2.4		In Service	
Maple				Wood					
Maple (II)	1945	1947	J. T. Taylor, Vancouver	Wood	11.5	3.1	2.0	1979	Ex 'Tahuna III'
Mary K				Wood					
Massett	1953	1953	F.S.M.D.	Wood	7.9	2.4	.7		
Mountain Ash	1926			Wood	9.1	2.3		1949	
Mountain Ash II	1948	1948	Falconer Marine, Victoria	Wood	6.7	2.4	.9		
Mountain Ash III	1973	1973	Fibreform	F.G.	6.8	2.4		In Service	Renamed 'Francis Lynn'
Negra				Wood					
Nerka				Wood					Cowichan Lake
Nesika	1933	1937	Herbert Gann	Wood	14.6	3.8	1.8	1974	
Nootka Forest	1978	1978	Rogers & Sinclair	Alum.	6.8	2.4		In Service	

Vessel	Year	Year	Builder	Material	Length	Beam	Draft	Disposition	Notes
Northern Scaler	1969	1969	Lynwood, Fort Langley	F.G.	8.5	2.7		1977	
Oak	1921	1921	Hoffar Brothers, Vancouver	Wood	9.1	2.4	.8	1949	Blimp
Oak II	1951	1951	F.S.M.D.	Wood	10.5	2.7	.9	1977	2nd Series Blimp
Ocean Falls				Wood					
Ocean Spray	1953	1953	F.S.M.D.	Wood	7.9	2.8	1.2	1979	
Oliver Clark	1925	1925	Rodd Brothers, Sidney	Wood	12.2	2.9			
Oliver Clark II	1939	1939	George Askew, Vancouver	Wood	17.0	4.4		In Service	Ex 'Leola Vivian', Ex 'B.C. Surveyor'
Ootsa Queen	1973	1974		Steel	9.1			In Service	Tug
Pacific Yew	1956	1956	F.S.M.D.	Wood	10.1	3.0		In Service	
Pauline				Wood					
Peace Ranger	1979	1979	Atlas Aluminum, Prince George	Alum.	9.3	3.0		In Service	
Pointer				Wood					
Popandi	1954			Wood				Circa 1956	Used on P.G.E. (Howe Sound)
Poplar	1912	1922	Falconer Marine	Wood	6.6	1.5	.8	1927	Ex 'Uaco'
Poplar II	1947	1947	Menchion Shipyard	Wood	7.9	2.7			
Poplar III	1948			Wood	14.6	4.1	1.1	In Service	Ex 'P.M.L. 17', Ex 'Otter'
Red Cedar	1918	1918	F.S., Thurston Bay	Wood	9.8	2.6	1.1		
Red Cedar II	1943	1943	F.S.M.D.	Wood	10.5	2.7	.9	In Service	2nd Series Blimp
Red Cedar III	1972	1972	Double Eagle	F.G.	5.6	2.2			
Rubra				Wood					
Rupert Scaler	1980	1980	Argo Marine Builders, Port Coquitlam	Alum.	6.1			In Service	2nd Series Blimp
Salal	1958	1958	F.S.M.D.	WOOD	7.0	2.4		Circa 1978	

Name	Date Built	Date Acq.	Builders	Mat'l	LOA	B	D	Date Disposed	Comments
Sanita	1910	1939	New Westminster, B.C.	Wood	19.3	3.7	2.3	1940	
Salt Mist	1929	1950	Vancouver	Wood	20.8	4.0	2.0	1963	Ex 'Kagome'
Sayward Forest	1978	1978	Sangster, Vancouver	F.G.	7.0	2.4		In Service	
Scaler	1924		F.S.M.D.	Wood	15.2				
Seedling	1957	1959		Wood	7.0			1979	
Sikanni Ranger	1977	1977	Howies Marine, Prince George	Alum.	7.3	2.1		In Service	
Silver Fir	1950	1950	F.S.M.D.	Wood	10.5	2.7	.9	1979	2nd Series Blimp
Sitka Spruce	1919	1919	F.S. Thurston Bay	Wood	9.8	2.6	1.1		
Sitka Spruce II	1952	1952	F.S.M.D.	Wood	10.5	2.7	.9	1977	2nd Series Blimp
R. J. Skinner	1909	1909	Vancouver Shipyards Ltd.	Wood	17.4	3.5	1.7	1924	
Sonora	1926	1926	F.S. Thurston Bay	Wood	8.8	2.3			
Sumac				Wood					
Swifter	1923	1923		Wood				1940	
Swifter II	1940	1940		Wood	7.9	2.5	.6	1949	
Sylva	1960	1960	F.S.M.D.	Wood	8.5	2.6			Babine Lake
Sycamore	1924	1924		Wood					
Syrene	1921	1942	J. Thorneycroft, England	Wood	25.9	4.0	2.4	1977	
Syringa	1946	1947	Falconer Marine	Wood	4.9	1.6			Interior Lake
Tachi				Wood					
Tachi II	1926	1926	Blake, Stewart Lake	Wood	9.1	2.3			
Tachi III	1950	1950	F.S.M.D.	Wood	9.9	3.1		1970	
Tachi IV	1970	1970	Pan-Yan Boats, N.Y.	F.G.	7.0	2.4	.7	In Service	
Tallyman				Wood					

Name	Built		Builder	Material	Length	Beam	Draft	Status	Notes
Tamarack	1927	1938	Charles Leslie, Vancouver	Wood	15.8	4.3	2.0	1976	Ex 'Miss Vivian'—B.C.P. #42
Tamarack II	1976	1976	Fibreform	F.G.	5.1	2.2		In Service	
Tempest	1978	1978	Sangster, North Vancouver	Wood	12.2			In Service	
Toba Forest	1910			F.G.	7.0	2.4	1.4		
Walrondo II	1927	1938	A. Linton & Co., Vancouver	Wood	10.4	2.9	1.5	1979	Rebuilt F.S.M.D. 1948, Ex 'Hermit'
Wells Gray	1950	1950	F.S.M.D.	Wood	14.7	3.5		1977	2nd Series Blimp
Western Ash				Wood	10.5	2.7	.9		
Western Hemlock				Wood	9.1				
Western Hemlock (II)	1958	1958	F.S.M.D.	Wood	12.2	3.4		In Service	
Western Yew	1946	1952	G.H. Oliver, North Vancouver	Wood	14.6	3.4		In Service	
White Birch	1950	1950	F.S.M.D.	Wood	10.5	2.7	.9	1978	2nd Series Blimp
White Cloud	1911	1942	Ah King, Hong Kong	Wood	18.3				
White Pine	1925	1925		Wood					
White Pine II	1915	1942	A.J. Jones, Kelowna	Wood	11.6	2.6	.9		Ex 'Princess Pat'
White Pine III	1948	1948	Falconer Marine	Wood	7.9	2.7	1.0		Destroyed by fire
White Pine IV	1958	1958	F.S.M.D.	Wood	7.0	2.4			
Whitesail	1958	1958	F.S.M.D.	Wood	13.7	2.4		1979	
White Spruce	1932	1945		Wood	13.1	3.0		1981	Ex 'Sea Belle III'
White Spruce II				Wood	11.3	3.0			Ex 'Hurrie' R.C.A.F.
White Spruce III				F.G.	5.5	2.3		In Service	
Wild Rose	1970	1970	Sangster, Vancouver	Wood	7.8	2.7	.6	Circa 1970	Babine Lake
Willow	1952	1952		Wood					
Willow	1920			Wood	5.5	1.8	.5	1978	
Willow II	1947			Steel	8.7	3.1			
Yarbeina	1972			Wood					
Yellow Cedar	1914	1948	Menchion Shipyard	Wood	16.1	4.7	1.7	In Service	Ex 'Bonila Rock', Rebuilt at Tofino, B.C. 1944

Name	Date Built	Date Acq.	Builders	Mat'l	Metres LOA	B	D	Date Disposed	Comments
Yellow Pine	1956	1956	F.S.M.D.	Wood	10.0	3.0		In Service	
Yew		1922		Wood					
Yew	1947	1947	Falconer Marine	Wood	4.9	1.7			Interior Lake
Yusella	1913	1927	Jancowski Brothers	Wood	11.4	2.7	.8		

Note 1: Historical data concerning the dimensions and other details of the older Forest Service boats are incomplete. I hope the reader will forgive the gaps in the above table; and in cases where he might have special knowledge, I invite him to submit data to the publisher for inclusion in subsequent editions of this book.

Note 2: In order to preserve the historical integrity of the text, imperial measurements of length were used. The metric equivalents are shown in the above table.